NONVERBAL LEARNING DISABILITIES AND THEIR CLINICAL SUBTYPES:

Assessment, Diagnosis and Management

A Handbook for Parents and Professionals
[Fourth Edition]

Maggie Mamen, Ph.D., C.Psych.

Published by:
Centrepointe Professional Services Inc.
98 Centrepointe Drive, Ottawa, Ontario, K2G 6B1, Canada

ISBN 0-9688279-0-X

info@centrepointepros.com

First Edition: September 2000
Second Edition: October 2000
Third Edition: July 2001
Fourth Edition: November 2002

TABLE OF CONTENTS

Overview

This handbook started out as the notes for presentations and handouts to groups of parents, educators and other professionals, and grew like Topsy. It is now in its greatly expanded Fourth Edition, primarily due to the many discussions I have been fortunate to be involved with all over the Province of Ontario and across provincial and national borders, and all the resulting ideas and suggestions that have been forthcoming from these various interactions and contacts.

Thanks to my colleagues at Centrepointe Professional Services (in particular, Dr. Joel Kanigsberg, Dr. Jody Alberts-Corush, Dr. Susan Rich, Judi Laurikainen, and Sally Lees), we have had many spirited and inspiring discussions over brown-bag lunches with respect to various clients who fill our caseloads. Brenda Case, our Educational Consultant, is a goldmine of ideas when it comes to teaching strategies and I am particularly grateful to her for a number of the suggestions for teachers contained in this handbook. She is also unflaggingly willing to help children with various learning problem through her diagnostic teaching, tutoring, and training activities.

We are all seeing more and more children who present with nonverbal deficits, and yearn to take time out of our busy practices to conduct the volumes of research on the ideas and hypotheses that our experiences continue to generate.

The classification of subtypes of nonverbal learning disabilities (NLD) is founded on clinical practice, not on empirically-based studies. Our experiences with clients of all ages tell us repeatedly that not all NLD children show the full range of difficulties that are contained in the literature on the NLD syndromes. For example, while many have noticeable social difficulties or problems with large muscle activities, still others are socially popular and athletically-talented. Separating out the major clusters of presenting issues is helpful in understanding, assessing, diagnosing, and managing individuals with learning disabilities

The major purpose of our involvement with these children, and therefore of this handbook, is to help parents and educators understand what is going on, where the strengths and weaknesses lie, and what they can do to assist these youngsters. We have discovered that grouping all NLD children under one "label" and attempting to generate a useful set of recommendations is an impossibility, since there appear to be as many differences within the group as there are between this group and other exceptionalities.

It is with this in mind that the handbook has been written. It is not meant to be exhaustive, but is intended to act as a "seed" paper to generate further debate and verification of the notion of subtypes of NLD. At the same time, it includes a number of suggestions that have appeared to be helpful in terms of addressing the needs of the various subtypes that we are proposing. The Fourth Edition has been considerably revised and expanded to include information on related disorders, additional case examples, notes on important issues to be considered in differential diagnosis, and further strategies for remediation and compensation.

I should like to acknowledge a very special debt of gratitude to the many parents and clients who have shared their very personal, and often quite distressing, experiences with me. These interactions keep this project alive and dynamic.

We are very open to further input, comments and even criticism! Please feel free to contact us at the address on the previous page, or via e-mail at: info@centrepointepros.com. Or you can check out our Website at: www.centrepointepros.com.

Copies of this handbook can be ordered by telephone (613 228-1174), by fax (613 228-2756), by email (info@centrepointepros.com) or by mail at 98 Centrepointe Drive, Ottawa, Ontario, K2G 6B1.

CHAPTER 1

GENERAL INTRODUCTION TO LEARNING DISABILITIES

Definition

While there have been many and varying attempts at definition, the general consensus is that a learning disability (LD) is the result of some disruption in the psychological processes basic to effective learning, in the context of at least average general cognitive functioning.

Recently, the Learning Disabilities Association of Ontario (LDAO), with support from the Government of Ontario, instituted the Promoting Early Identification Project, encompassing issues such as definition, screening, assessment, programming, and teacher education with respect to learning disabilities in general. The following definition was adopted by the LDAO in the summer of 2001.

> *"Learning Disabilities" refers to a variety of disorders that affect the acquisition, retention, understanding, organization or use of verbal and/or non-verbal information. These disorders result from impairments in one or more psychological processes related to learning* in combination with otherwise average abilities essential for thinking and reasoning. Learning disabilities are specific not global impairments and as such are distinct from intellectual disabilities.*
>
> *Learning disabilities range in severity and invariably interfere with the acquisition and use of one or more of the following important skills:*
> *oral language (e.g., listening, speaking, understanding)*
> *reading (e.g., decoding, comprehension)*
> *written language (e.g., spelling, written expression)*
> *mathematics (e.g., computation, problem solving)*
> *Learning disabilities may also cause difficulties with organizational skills, social perception and social interaction.*

The impairments are generally life-long. However, their effects may be expressed differently over time, depending on the match between the demands of the environment and the individual's characteristics. Some impairments may be noted during the pre-school years, while others may not become evident until much later. During the school years, learning disabilities are suggested by unexpectedly low academic achievement or achievement that is sustainable only by extremely high levels of effort and support.

Learning disabilities are due to genetic, other congenital and/or acquired neuro-biological factors. They are not caused by factors such as cultural or language differences, inadequate or inappropriate instruction, socio-economic status or lack of motivation, although any one of these and other factors may compound the impact of learning disabilities. Frequently learning disabilities co-exist with other conditions, including attentional, behavioural and emotional disorders, sensory impairments or other medical conditions.

For success, persons with learning disabilities require specialized interventions in home, school, community and workplace settings, appropriate to their individual strengths and needs, including:
specific skills instruction;
the development of compensatory strategies;
the development of self-advocacy skills;
appropriate accommodations.

**The term "psychological processes" describes an evolving list of cognitive functions. To date, research has focused on functions such as: phonological processing; memory and attention; processing speed; language processing; perceptual-motor processing; visual-spatial processing; executive functions (e.g., planning, monitoring and metacognitive abilities).*

This definition is supported by a background document entitled: "Operationalizing the New Definition of Learning Disabilities for Utilization within Ontario's Educational System," LDAO, 2001.

The definition itself does not differentiate language-based learning disabilities (LLD) from nonverbal learning disabilities (NLD). It is, however, generally understood that individuals with LLD show deficits in language-based and language-related psychological processes, whereas individuals with NLD are more likely to show deficits in nonverbal psychological processes, such as visual, spatial and/or motor functioning.

Making the "Learning Cake"

In order to help understand the concept of learning disabilities, an analogy provides more familiar terms.

Learning is like baking a cake. All cakes have a basic set of ingredients; so does learning. This is where the "thinking and reasoning skills" come in. The more we have, the bigger the cake we can make. Each different type of cake, or learning situation, requires additional ingredients, which will vary, depending on the anticipated outcome.

If any of the ingredients are missing, the cake will not turn out as planned – may fail completely, in fact. It may be possible to substitute some similar ingredient that may work as well, or almost as well. We may be able to substitute a visual approach to a reading task, if a child is lacking good auditory skills, for example. We may be able to memorize something we cannot reason through, or we may be able to work out something we cannot memorize.

In addition to having all the ingredients, or suitable substitutes, it is important to have the ingredients in the correct proportions. If a child has 25 kg of flour, but no eggs, the cake will flop – badly. Giving the child more and more flour and encouraging him to use it will not make the cake turn out any better. In fact, the balance of ingredients will become worse, and people may become even more impatient that the cake is not successful. Parents and teachers alike are puzzled when a child who seems quite gifted verbally, and whose remaining skills are average for his age, simply cannot learn well. For NLD children, it is the sometimes more subtle nonverbal ingredients that are insufficient; for LLD children, it is the sometimes more obvious language-based ones.

We may have all the ingredients in the world available to us, but we may be stuck unless we follow the *recipe*, without which we do not know which of the ingredients to use, in what proportion, in what order we need to combine them, and what we are supposed to do with them. For many NLD individuals, it is not so much *what* they do, but *how* they do it that causes problems.

When we assess a particular child, individual skills may well appear to be present, perhaps even in reasonably adequate proportions, and we may not always see the huge discrepancies between aptitude and achievement, or between the different aptitudes, that are commonly anticipated in children with learning disabilities. However, watching these children perform, their difficulties with the recipe are glaringly obvious. However, it is quite difficult, if not impossible, to measure or quantify the *process* by which a child learns. Thus, experience, astute observation, and our own reactions to working or living with NLD children play a vital part in the understanding of these youngsters.

Language Learning Disabilities (LLD)

For a child to be diagnosed with a language-based learning disability, his thinking and reasoning skills must be within the broad average range, with deficits in at least one major aspect of linguistic processing that can be directly related to his learning problems. For children with auditory and/or language processing problems, it is quite likely to be nonverbal reasoning skills (e.g., pattern recognition, analysis/synthesis, visual concept formation, part-whole concepts, etc.) that are assessed as being strengths. Some children with LLD do well on verbal reasoning tasks, however, on some tests where leeway is given for imprecise expressive language. For example, a child who is asked to explain how a firefighter and a police officer are alike might say: "Him wear clothes like each other. Get him out of cars because they crash." Deficits in linguistic/auditory processing could include problems with discrimination of sounds, short-term or long-term auditory memory, central auditory processing, sequencing of sounds, development of ideas, receptive and/or expressive vocabulary, syntax, semantics, listening comprehension, sound/symbol correspondence, phonological awareness, and so on.

Difficulties in primary language processing (such as auditory discrimination of linguistically-meaningful sounds, blending of sounds into words, understanding and development of vocabulary and syntax, comprehension of verbally-presented information, organizing linguistic output, and so on) are most often associated with learning problems in the acquisition of secondary language skills, most notably reading and other language-based arts. It is, of course, important to remember that mathematics has a complex "language" of its own. There are children who may have an excellent grasp of such concepts as quantity, sets, time, space, measurement, but who do not understand that "minus," "take away," "less than," "gives one to," etc., are synonymous and represent a particular mathematical operation.

Students whose auditory and/or linguistic processes interfere with their learning are traditionally labeled as learning disabled (LD) or language learning disabled (LLD), and various remedial approaches have been available for these children for some time. The services of speech-language pathologists are invaluable for assessment, therapy, and consultation with respect to learning needs and teaching strategies.

Differences between LLD and NLD

The following table illustrates the basic differences between LLD and NLD.

LANGUAGE LEARNING DISABILITIES	***NONVERBAL LEARNING DISABILITIES***
Frequently show strengths in most or all	
nonverbal thinking and reasoning abilities visual pattern recognition analysis/synthesis of spatial information visual concept formation nonverbal part-whole concepts spatial reasoning short-term and long-term visual memory visual-motor integration fine motor skills visual perception tactile perception	vocabulary development general knowledge oral presentation, verbal fluency auditory attention sound discrimination short-term auditory memory long-term auditory memory sequencing of sounds organization of ideas when presenting orally syntax listening comprehension phonological awareness

<table>
<tr><th colspan="2">Commonly present with weaknesses in one or more</th></tr>
<tr><td>receptive and/or expressive vocabulary
auditory attention
sound discrimination
short-term auditory memory
long-term auditory memory
central auditory processing
sequencing of sounds
organization of ideas in words
syntax
semantics
listening comprehension
phonological awareness</td><td>nonverbal thinking and reasoning abilities
pattern recognition and reproduction
visual concept formation
part-whole concepts
analysis of complex tasks into component parts
spatial reasoning, directionality
concepts of time, space, distance, speed
short-term and long-term visual memory
visual-motor integration
motor planning and fine motor skills
visual perception
tactile perception</td></tr>
<tr><th colspan="2">Generally leading to difficulties in the following areas</th></tr>
<tr><td>early reading acquisition
sound/symbol correspondence
decoding
phonics
written language
  composition, sequencing of ideas
  use of appropriate vocabulary
oral presentations
oral responses in class
mathematics
  language of math
  word problems
social skills
behaviour</td><td>reading comprehension
mathematics
  math concepts
  relationships among numbers
  measurement
  geometry, trigonometry
  graphs, diagrams
maps
organizational skills
  time management
  project management
  management of personal belongings, space
social skills
behaviour</td></tr>
</table>

CHAPTER 2

RECOGNIZING NLD

It has long been accepted that communication skills are substantially nonverbal, some would claim to the tune of 90%. It should not, therefore, come as a surprise that disruptions in nonverbal psychological processes can affect a range of learning tasks, perhaps even to a greater, albeit more subtle, extent than disruptions in language-based abilities.

The concept of nonverbal learning disabilities (NLD) has been around for more than three decades, primarily stemming from the work of Byron Rourke and his colleagues from the University of Windsor (e.g., Rourke, 1995), who have proposed a "syndrome" of NLD that is broad and encompassing. Surprisingly, although much of the literature deals with adults for whom nonverbal deficits are secondary to certain types of acute brain damage, NLD as an educational phenomenon is still in its infancy, especially in terms of differential diagnosis and remedial planning. The work of Sue Thompson has been important in providing recognition and a wide range of recommendations for dealing with NLD children in the school system (Thompson, 1997). Further detailed information can be obtained from the following websites: www.nldontheweb.org and www.nldline.com.

For NLD children, the recipe – or knowledge of the appropriate process of learning – is frequently missing. Many of them do not even know what cake they are making, let alone what tools to use, when to use them, or how to use them. They often depend on adults to tell them – which adults usually do. This reliance on others may well become entrenched to the point that they may develop quite an entourage - parents, teachers, teacher's aide, resource teacher, tutor, study buddy, and so on – to help cue them as to what to do when.

In addition to difficulties with the process of learning, probably the most significant deficits in individuals with NLD are difficulties with *pattern recognition* – visual, social, motor, auditory, behavioural, and so on, making it hard to apply what has been perceived in one situation to another, similar situation, and meaning that, unless translated into the familiar and comfortable verbal medium, the world is over-stimulating, chaotic, and essentially meaningless.

NLD affects most non-linguistic aspects of communication; for example:

- interpretation of visual social cues, such as body language, gestures, facial expressions;
- understanding of tone of voice, mood, emotional cues;
- comprehension of information not immediately contained in words, such as nuances, humour, sarcasm, metaphor, imagery;
- the pragmatics of language, particularly social language: knowing what another party knows or needs to know, what to say when, when and how to initiate and maintain conversations, when and how to terminate communication, and so on.

In addition, deficits are frequently found in the following, more general, areas of functioning:

- general organizational abilities; most specifically, in the ability to break down a complex task into its component parts and to work through the steps in order to complete the task;
- difficulties with part-whole relationships;
- mastery of nonverbal mathematical concepts such as time, space, quantity, visual array;
- ability to grasp and manipulate spatial relationships in one-, two- and three-dimensions;
- understanding of the position of self in space, orientation, directionality;
- visual pattern recognition and memory;
- visual-motor integration and fine motor control.

When taken together, the overall pattern of difficulties for individuals with NLD tends to involve most or all of the following major areas of functioning: ***INTERPRETATION***, ***INTEGRATION***, ***INTUITION***, ***INSIGHT***, ***INITIATIVE and INDEPENDENCE***. Unfortunately, none of these is particularly easy to teach, and we frequently need to seek exceedingly concrete ways in which to help individuals with NLD to compensate for these weaknesses, while at the same time encouraging their self-reliance.

The overwhelming impact of deficits in these areas on the life of the NLD individual is consistently underestimated.

Presenting Issues

In general, the presenting issues in children with NLD tend to be as follows:

- behavioural, social and/or emotional concerns, not academic issues
- difficulties with pattern recognition
- strengths in verbal areas
- deficits in nonverbal psychological processes (e.g., visual, spatial, motor, tactile)
- difficulties with executive functions (planning, self-monitoring, self-regulation, etc.)
- problems with organizational skills
- trouble understanding concepts of time, distance, space, direction,
- personal boundaries.

It is normally not unless, or until, a psychological or psychoeducational assessment is undertaken that the child's cognitive profile reveals the nonverbal deficits and processing problems that underlie many of the behavioural, social and learning difficulties experienced in the school environment and beyond. It is therefore critical, if a diagnosis of NLD is to be considered, that a full psychological assessment be conducted, including cognitive testing, behavioural observations, full parent and teacher interviews, visual-motor assessment (Occupational Therapy involvement has often already been initiated with these children), social skills screening and some personality assessment. Testing instruments are sometimes somewhat limiting when attempting to assess for NLD in young children. These children's strengths and weaknesses would be better pinpointed were it possible to assess in any reliable, valid and standardized way kinesthetic intelligence, musical intelligence, inter- and intrapersonal intelligence, and "emotional intelligence," in addition to the more common tests of verbal, quantitative and visual-spatial abilities available at the present time.

Adding to the confusion is the fact that many NLD children have such strong, sometimes superior or very superior, verbal abilities, that they are frequently an enigma to those who live with and teach them, and it is often extremely hard for parents, teachers and others to come to terms with the fact that there may be a learning disability of any kind.

Verbal strength may be used both as a defence and as a weapon, and NLD children are sometimes viewed as "mouthy," overly verbose, or even verbally aggressive. Since expressive vocabulary is usually seen by most people as a reliable predictor of a person's general "intelligence," children with NLD are frequently expected to perform as uniformly competently as they appear to be from their "superficial" verbal abilities. They may well talk their way into many situations for which they do not possess the substantive follow-through, and their facility with words may result in the delegation of more responsibility than they are actually able to handle. Frustration is thus a very common, a natural result of the discrepancy between expectation and reality, on the part of both the NLD child and those around him.

Because of difficulties recognizing and interpreting visual cues, including facial expressions and gestures, and because of problems adjusting their verbal output (e.g., vocabulary, tone of voice, subject of conversation, turn-taking, etc.) to be appropriate for different circumstances, children with NLD frequently encounter difficulties in a variety of social situations. While they may interact relatively well with adults and younger children, they often have problems maintaining friendships with their age peers.

Language Difficulties in NLD

Despite the fact that the primary focus of NLD lies, by definition, in nonverbal psychological process deficits, there are a number of language skills that are affected. Pattern recognition is critical when processing verbal input – not simply to recognize the sounds of the words so that they can be linked directly with what they mean, but also to recognize the myriad of nonverbal information that helps us understand more than the words. These patterns include the following.

(a) ***Tone of voice, loudness, pace:*** these help us understand the speaker's feelings, intention, mood, and so forth, and may indicate more complex emotional factors, such as degree of intimacy, respect, and other interpersonal information; most of us have had occasion to say: "it's not *what* you said, it's *how* you said it." When we increase the pace of our speech, we are usually indicating urgency, and frequently intend to communicate a need to hurry.

(b) ***Emphasis on a particular word or phrase:*** we need to know the difference between, for example, "I *WANT* to come later" and "I want to come *LATER*," if we are to anticipate someone else's actions and respond appropriately.

(c) ***Use of sarcasm, irony, humour, etc.:*** particularly in social situations, we need to know when someone means what they are saying, or whether they are teasing. For example, saying: "Oh, *THAT'S* a really intelligent thing to say!" and meaning the opposite, will be lost on many NLD individuals.

(d) ***Use of analogy, metaphor:*** most individuals with NLD are quite concrete in their language – they say what they mean, and they mean what they say, and they assume that everyone else does. So, when we say: "It's raining cats and dogs," they look for them. Metaphors such as the "learning cake" may well be lost on them, and they wonder why people are talking about flour and eggs when they want to know why they are having problems with their learning.

(e) ***Turn-taking in conversation:*** because of their good vocabulary and general knowledge, most individuals with NLD can "hold forth" and conduct monologues on a number of topics, without recognizing or acknowledging that true communicative language requires a response from the other party or parties; having an idea of how long one can speak before letting another person have a turn is a nonverbal skill;

(f) ***Body language:*** there are certain unwritten "rules" regarding how we act when we are speaking that assist others to interpret the meaning of what we are saying; for example, making and maintaining appropriate eye contact, physical distance from the speaker, touching someone as we speak, "tightness" of body (e.g., arms folded, jaw clenched, shoulders shrugged, etc.).

(g) ***Facial expressions:*** these are often critical in determining the speaker's feelings; recognizing that someone is frowning, smiling, closing eyes, rolling eyes, pursing lips, raising an eyebrow, widening eyes, winking, clenching cheek muscles, are all very important in this regard;

these expressions are also helpful in figuring out whether an individual is projecting the same feeling as that expressed in the words they are speaking, or their tone of voice.

(h) ***Rhythm, rhyme:*** these are non-word aspect of language that are especially important in the early stages of reading acquisition, in order that a child can learn to recognize patterns of language that will help to predict what is coming next; they are also important memory aids.

Early Identification of NLD

The early identification of NLD, especially in younger children, has traditionally presented some problems. This is primarily because these youngsters quite frequently, if not almost exclusively, present initially with difficulties other than the academic lags traditionally seen in the LLD population. Behaviour problems, social difficulties, low frustration tolerance, verbal abuse, poor or non-existent written work are just some of the presenting issues that bring such children to the attention of psychological or social service providers, particularly in the first few grades. It is not uncommon for there to be few, or even no, worries on the part of teachers regarding academic progress during the primary years. Given the nature of NLD, in that it often affects the *integration* of basic skills, rather than their *acquisition*, academics are not usually significantly affected until Grade 3 or Grade 4. It is at this point that the emphasis in the classroom switches from straightforward skill mastery to the need to choose which skills to use in order to address more complex academics, specifically reading comprehension, math problem-solving and creative writing.

Risk Factors in Preschool Children

While none of the following is a specific or definitive indication of potential NLD problems, and many of them are common in early childhood, the continuing presence of one or more may well be a risk factor requiring careful monitoring and possible assessment.

Active avoidance of fine motor activities (e.g., colouring, drawing, puzzles, Lego, etc.)

Problems with pattern recognition/reproduction (e.g., musical, visual)
Difficulties with subtle aspects of language (e.g., humour, analogy, symbolic language, etc.)
Poor social use of language
Misinterpretation of visual cues, social cues
Poor social interactions
Hypersensitivity to visual, tactile stimulation
Problems with gross motor activities (e.g., balance, laterality)
Eye-hand coordination difficulties.

Familial Factors

Research has long indicated that learning disabilities tend to run in families, whether this is due to genetic heritability factors, social learning, habit, or a combination of these. There is, therefore, a good probability that one or both parents of a youngster with NLD will also themselves show some signs of NLD. In addition, there are clearly teachers who exhibit a pattern of attributes consistent with NLD, and who rely heavily on their verbal skills to manage the day-to-day issues that arise. It is important to bear this in mind when attempting to explain NLD, helping parents understand what the implications are, and suggesting strategies that might help. The use of analogies, body language, subtle nonverbal indications of expectations, or other nonverbal cues, needs to be monitored, and it will be necessary to check out regularly that good communication has, in fact, taken place, in order to prevent misunderstandings and misinterpretations. Ensuring that verbal communication is direct, clear, and free from ambiguities, will be most helpful.

CHAPTER 3

ASSESSMENT AND DIAGNOSIS OF NLD

General Issues in Diagnosis

The diagnosis of any type of learning disability or other condition can be important for many reasons: validation of a parent's and/or teacher's concerns; explanation of a group of symptoms and signs; provision of a statement regarding causal factors; acquisition of funding for special education; class placement; eligibility for disability allowances; access to program modifications and accommodation; provision of a direction for intervention; understanding of the longer term implications; explanation as to why previous interventions may not have been successful, and so on.

In Ontario, under the provisions of the Regulated Health Professions Act (1993), the act of *communicating* a diagnosis is considered to be a "controlled act" because it has potential for harm. Consider the implications of an error in diagnosis that could lead to inappropriate intervention or to no intervention at all. Thus, only *appropriately qualified* members of the College of Psychologists of Ontario, and the College of Physicians and Surgeons of Ontario, are given the legal mandate to perform the controlled act of diagnosis.

As with other childhood conditions, there are frequently many professionals, as well as parents, who are familiar with a range of problem areas and who are well able to provide an opinion or a judgement as to what might be the cause of a child's difficulties. In these days of the Internet, in particular, many of us are very well read and informed, particularly if there is clearly something affecting our children that we feel some responsibility to fix. Because of different biases in knowledge and training, the probability of a particular opinion being given, even with the same symptom presentation, will vary depending on the background of the particular professional involved. For example, while a psychological service provider may interpret a given set of symptoms as NLD, a psychiatrist or neurologist may see the same set as Asperger's Syndrome, an occupational therapist as a Developmental Coordination Disorder, and a speech-language pathologist as a Pragmatic Language Disorder. It is not uncommon for parents of children with NLD to receive more than one, apparently conflicting, diagnosis.

It is important to be aware that a specific diagnosis is not a prerequisite to providing assistance for a child with academic or behavioural issues. Even if a child's difficulties do not meet specific diagnostic requirements, an understanding of the pattern of strengths and weaknesses can help determine appropriate remedial and compensatory strategies, even for children whose impairments are relatively mild.

Diagnostic Indicators of NLD

The first concrete diagnostic indicator that NLD may well be present is found in the child's cognitive profile, as measured by one of the standardized tests, such as the Wechsler Scales, the Woodcock-Johnson Tests of Cognitive Ability, the Stanford-Binet, the Kaufman Assessment Battery for Children, or other such battery. The most typical pattern on the Wechsler scales, for example, shows a *significant* discrepancy between the Verbal and Performance scales, in favour of the former. In other words, the NLD child may show relatively few, if any, deficits on verbal comprehension subtests, and perhaps would even be seen as strong, very strong or sometimes even gifted in areas such as general knowledge, verbal concept formation, vocabulary and social problem-solving. The latter (for example, the WISC-III Comprehension subtest) may well be particularly important in the differential diagnosis of Asperger's Syndrome and this will be discussed below.

As explained in more detail under the different subtypes below, while a Verbal-Performance split is usually a starting point for suspecting NLD, it is important to examine the detailed psychoeducational profile before proceeding with further differential diagnosis. There are a number of children with NLD who do *not* show a significant discrepancy between their Verbal and Performance scales, sometimes due to an outlying subtest score or two. For example, some children score extremely low on the verbal subtests measuring numerical reasoning and/or social problem-solving, which will reduce the overall verbal composite score. Others may produce an extremely high score on the nonverbal subtests measuring visual attention and/or visual-motor speed, thus raising the performance composite score. When using the Wechsler Intelligence Scale for Children (Third Edition), or WISC-III, it is often more useful to compare Index scores for Verbal Comprehension and Perceptual Organization, or Verbal Comprehension and Processing Speed, rather than to examine only the Verbal-Performance discrepancy.

Other children's test performance is affected more by *how* they perform the test, not *what* they say or do, resulting in scores that are not particularly different from the norm for their age, but reflecting a somewhat circuitous route to get there. Still others are more ponderous, and slower to perform any test that is timed, and it is important to differentiate those children who are successful on all items but who do not gain bonus time points from those who perform some items very quickly but make errors on others. This appears to be especially necessary for children from about age 13 and up, since even one time bonus point can sometimes make a difference of two standard score points.

For clinicians, it is vitally important to take a broader look at the child's *overall* presenting profile, including anecdotal information from parents and teachers, and to observe the individual's behaviour extremely carefully during the course of the assessment in order to pick up important processing difficulties that may not be reflected in the actual scores themselves.

It is fairly characteristic of individuals with NLD that they score relatively well when tested on individual academic sub-skills. For example, when they are tested on spelling, or multiplication, or definitions, they may appear to be quite average or even better. Even when they are found to be deficient in a specific area, they can sometimes be remediated in that specific area with some apparent degree of success. However, they do not appear to generalize or to be able to use these skills in more complex task areas. This emphasizes the fact that it is the *integration* of the skills that reflects the deficits, and not the specific level of ability *per se*. The integration aspects are sometimes difficult to measure objectively, and often must be inferred.

It is important to emphasize that a much broader range of observational and anecdotal information be gathered, rather than limiting assessment to formal testing alone.

Criteria for Diagnosis of NLD

Under the definition of Learning Disability outlined earlier, the following criteria would need to be met for a diagnosis of a nonverbal learning disability:

(a) Thinking and reasoning skills at least average

This means that there should be documented evidence that the individual has at least one major area of thinking and reasoning that reaches the criterion for "average." For most widely-used tests, this is usually taken to mean a standard score of 80 or above, although many practitioners prefer to use the cut-off of one standard deviation, which is usually a standard score of 85 or above. It is important to note that there are many measures of "thinking and reasoning" skills, and clinicians need to be prepared to back up their opinions with more than one test result. However, contrary to popular lay belief, an individual's overall IQ score is not, in and of itself, a valid measure, unless, of course, it is in the average range or above. In other words, an overall IQ score that is below the 80-85 range does not mean that an individual does not have some major measures of thinking and reasoning that fall within the average band. For most NLD children, the strength(s) in thinking and reasoning are most likely to be found in the verbal areas – in measures of abstract and/or applied reasoning abilities. However, particularly those children whose difficulties are primarily visual-motor may well have a strong score or two on measures of abstract verbal reasoning, such as the Block Design subtest of the WISC-III, although, clearly, one single score is insufficient evidence for diagnostic reasons. The Woodcock-Johnson III, for example, has a subscale called "Thinking Ability" that takes into account both verbal and nonverbal reasoning, which can be compared with either Verbal Ability or Cognitive Efficiency, the latter of which is frequently weak in NLD children.

(b) ***Impairments in psychological processes related to learning***

This means that there should be documented evidence that the individual has measurable impairment in at least one major area of nonverbal processing, including, but not limited to, visual/motor/tactile memory and attention; visual-motor and/or fine motor processing speed; pragmatic language difficulties; perceptual-motor processing; visual-spatial processing; executive functions (e.g., planning, monitoring and metacognitive abilities). These processing impairments should be logically connected to the individual's actual, observable learning deficits, in terms of being ***causal*** in nature. The range of potential assessment instruments to measure nonverbal psychological processes is, of course, quite broad, although it is hard to find measures that are free from the ubiquitous verbal mediation that assists most of us to solve problems. However, in general, a thorough assessment would include measures of visual-spatial processes (attention, short-term memory, long-term memory, accuracy/speed, discrimination, sequencing, etc.), fine motor ability (speed, dexterity, laterality, etc.), visual-motor integration (copying of linguistic and nonlinguistic stimuli, eye-hand coordination, etc.), executive functioning (planning ability, etc.), in addition to basic language testing that could tease out pragmatics from other, more obvious verbal abilities, such as vocabulary and general knowledge. Many of these psychological processes are, of course, measured in the course of a basic cognitive assessment. While a single, low composite, index, or single scaled score is often indicative of significant weakness, it is necessary to provide further back-up with additional assessment data, observation and/or reports from other professionals.

Documentation of a Learning Disability

Both parents and teachers alike are frequently concerned about the information contained (or not contained) in psychological and psychoeducational reports. Under the guidelines drafted by the Screening and Assessment Subcommittee of the Promoting Early Identification Project, and also on the guidelines published by the Ontario Psychological Association, thorough assessment and documentation are required in support of a diagnosis of any type of learning disability. These guidelines are as follows:

> *Any diagnostic report should include all of the following components, unless a valid rationale is provided for not doing so.*
>
> *Information about home language use (original language, dialect, language(s) spoken in the home, etc.)*
>
> *Relevant medical/developmental/family history, including results of any vision/hearing evaluations*

Educational history, including information about remedial programs, special class placements, or other support that have been provided

Relevant information from other professional evaluations (e.g., speech-language, occupational therapy, educational consultant, etc.), including previous psychological assessments

A statement regarding the validity of the assessment

Behavioural observations during the testing session, as well as available observations (both anecdotal and from rating scales) from parents, teachers, classroom visits, etc.

Reporting and interpretation of formal test results, including a description of the individual's strengths and needs, an indication of how the observed pattern of abilities and achievement demonstrates the presence of a specific disability, and adequately documented evidence as to the cause of the learning difficulties

A specific, clear, diagnostic statement that the individual has a Learning Disability

Based on the individual's strengths and needs, recommendations/suggestions/indications for further action and intervention in the areas of skill instruction, compensatory strategies, and self-advocacy skills, along with requirements for appropriate accommodations at home, and in school, community and/or workplace settings

Signature of an appropriately qualified member of the College of Psychologists of Ontario (CPO) or the College of Physicians and Surgeons of Ontario (CPSO). The qualified member must be present (preferably in person, or in real-time audio or visual connection) when oral diagnostic reports are delivered.

Note: Appropriately documented, informed consent for psychological assessment must be obtained in advance from the individual concerned, or from his or her parents or legal guardians, by the individual who will be conducting the assessment. In addition to information regarding the assessment procedures themselves, such informed consent must include an explanation regarding: the potential release of information and/or the report to any third party; the potential distribution and storage of the assessment information and documentation, including circulation within a school system or inclusion in the Ontario Student Record (OSR); the individual's rights regarding withholding or withdrawal of consent; and the right of direct access to the qualified member of the CPO or CPSO who is responsible for the diagnosis.

Many assessment reports contain profession-specific jargon or mumbo-jumbo that means nothing to those individuals who must use these documents to support everything from special education placements to parenting interventions to disability insurance claims. "So what?" is probably the most frequently asked question, after "What does this word mean?" It behooves the author to communicate information in a way that it can be understood by its audience. We are way beyond the time when psychologists and others wrote reports only for physicians or other psychological service providers. Parents are almost always the child's primary case managers, and as such need to be able to understand clearly what the results of a report mean. This means that it is insufficient to say, for example, "his perceptual organizational skills are below average." It is vital that everyone understands what this statement ***implies or predicts or connects with*** in terms of an individual's daily life at school, at home, or elsewhere.

It is necessary to be confident to approach the author of the report for an explanation of anything that is not understood, for clarification of terms, and for questions regarding the implications of any statements contained therein.

It is also critical to remember that the individual frequently reads his or her own report – maybe not immediately if he or she is a child, but potentially in several years' time. It is a reasonable rule-of-thumb for professionals never to write anything that they would not be comfortable with a client reading.

Practitioners should never forget that an assessment is an intervention, and as such can have far-reaching consequences.

CHAPTER 4

NLD AND RELATED DISORDERS

There are many factors that impact a person's ability to learn. These factors include both intrinsic and extrinsic issues, including genetics, motivation, level of environmental stimulation, language of instruction, family crises, chaotic and/or dysfunctional family situation, separation and divorce, physical or mental illness, problems with hearing or vision, inadequate instructional opportunities, and so on. It is not the purpose of this module to explore any of these – simply to ensure that there is an awareness that a nonverbal learning disability is only one of a number of factors that should be considered in the presence of learning difficulties.

There are also a number of childhood disorders that may present similar concerns, and there is currently much debate with respect to differential diagnoses among these various categories. Again, the purpose of this learning module is not to resolve this debate, nor even to present each issue in details. The following will simply introduce you to some other disorders and outline the main commonalities and differences. For many youngsters, a full, often multidisciplinary, assessment is necessary for a competent differential diagnosis to be made.

Nonetheless, the strategies outlined later in this module can, and probably should, be applied, regardless of the specific diagnosis, if it is felt that the child is experiencing difficulties in some of the nonverbal areas. The degree of success of the intervention, however, may well differ, depending on the underlying cause of the problem.

Mild Intellectual Disabilities and Developmental Delay

Children whose abilities essential to thinking and reasoning are assessed to be *globally* below average, and whose cognitive-developmental milestones are lagging behind their peers, are classified as either mildly intellectually disabled (MID) or developmentally disabled (DD), depending upon the degree of impairment. They tend to have difficulties in all academic areas. Appropriate interventions are generally slower paced, developmentally based, and geared to the acquisition of basic literacy and numeracy, as well as adaptive behavioural, communication, and life skills.

There is a small subset of children who appear to meet criteria for both MID and LD. These are children whose overall cognitive abilities fall within the borderline range (standard scores of 70-80), perhaps even showing borderline scores for composite scales, such as the verbal and performance scales of the Wechsler tests. However, examination of the individual subtests may show high variability, with some measures of thinking and reasoning abilities falling within the broad range of average (between 80 and 90). The main issue with these children is that they may require *both* specialized teaching to take advantage of their relative strengths and remediate their specific weaknesses, *as well as* a slower pace of learning and modified academic expectations.

Children who fall within the developmentally disabled range (cognitive abilities at the 1st percentile or below) require very specific programming, geared to basic survival literacy and adaptive skills. While on occasion they show "splinter" strengths (e.g., in short-term rote memory), it is highly unlikely that any measure of their thinking and reasoning skills falls within even the broad range of average.

Asperger's Syndrome

Asperger's Syndrome (AS) and NLD are often confused, with some authors and practitioners not differentiating at all, others perceiving them as different points along a continuum, and still others seeing them as different, albeit overlapping, disorders (e.g., Stewart, 2002). The major similarity between the two is that both involve difficulties with social interaction and interpersonal skills. The major difference is that AS is an *autistic-spectrum*, pervasive developmental disorder, with chronically restricted repetitive and stereotyped patterns of behaviour, interests, and activities, which are far beyond the narrow range of activities, social awkwardness, and slightly eccentric behaviours that are sometimes found in individuals with NLD.

The diagnostic criteria for Asperger's Disorder from the Diagnostic and Statistical Manual IV (DSM-IV) of the American Psychiatric Association are listed as:

A. Qualitative impairment in social interaction, as manifested by at least two of the following:

(1) marked impairment in the use of multiple nonverbal behaviours such as eye-to-eye gaze, facial expression, body postures, and gestures to regulate social interaction

(2) failure to develop peer relationships appropriate to developmental level

(3) a lack of spontaneous seeking to share enjoyment, interests, or achievements with other people (e.g., by a lack of showing, bringing, or pointing out objects of interest to other people)
(4) lack of social or emotional reciprocity

B. Restricted repetitive and stereotyped patterns of behaviour, interests, and activities, as manifested by at least one of the following:
(1) encompassing preoccupation with one or more stereotyped and restricted patterns of interest that is abnormal either in intensity or focus
(2) apparently inflexible adherence to specific, nonfunctional routines or rituals
(3) stereotyped and repetitive motor mannerisms (e.g., hand or finger flapping or twisting, or complex whole-body movements)
(4) persistent preoccupation with parts of objects

C. The disturbance causes clinically significant impairment in social, occupational, or other important areas of functioning.

D. There is no clinically significant general delay in language (e.g., single words used by age 2 years, communicative phrases used by age 3 years).

E. There is no clinically significant delay in cognitive development or in the development of age-appropriate self-help skills, adaptive behaviour (other than social interaction), and curiosity about the environment in childhood.

F. Criteria are not met for another specific Pervasive Developmental Disorder or Schizophrenia.

Caution should always be exercised when a diagnosis of either Asperger's Syndrome (especially "mild" AS) or NLD is given based on an individual's difficulties with social skills and interpersonal interactions. While both disorders certainly may have this common element, and may indeed co-exist in some individuals, it is important that a full psychological assessment is conducted to determine whether there is an underlying learning disability profile that may well be affecting other, more subtle aspects of the individual's life, particularly in academic areas.

When it comes to remediation, one of the major factors that seems to differentiate Asperger's children from S-NLD youngsters is the ability and motivation to acquire social knowledge. Children with S-NLD appear to benefit appreciably from social skills remediation, either in a one-on-one, pragmatic-language-based program, or in small group settings with opportunities for role play, and re-testing on measures of social comprehension often indicates significant gains. Asperger's children, on the other hand, do not appear to learn as quickly, if at all, since the motivation to interact is often lacking, even in a one-on-one situation, and in our clinical observations they tend not to show improvement on psychometric measures of social cognition from pre- to post-testing. In addition, Asperger's children tend to exhibit autistic-like behaviours, including some stereotypic behaviours, perseveration, self-absorption, fixation on parts of objects or themes, and so on, which are not seen in children with NLD.

Attention Deficit Disorders (ADD, AD/HD)

Many individuals with LD exhibit symptoms of attentional difficulties, most notably distractibility, short attention span, impulsivity, difficulties with self-regulation, excessive motor movement, poor working memory, tendency to "day dream" or "tune out," and so on, sometimes accompanied by acting-out behaviours. In the case of NLD, the individual is specifically over-stimulated by visual and tactile input. In other words, a child may be overwhelmed by the visual environment, or may be inordinately distracted by the feel of clothing, the texture of food, or the sensations of finger paints. In such circumstances, he will respond to the stress in his own intrinsic way – either by "fight" (i.e., engage in behaviours that are external, obvious and intended to engage others), by "flight" (i.e., engage in behaviours that take him away from the stressful situation, such as day-dreaming), or by "freeze," which puts him total shut-down mode.

It is extremely important to understand that many LD children who show clear symptoms of attentional problems and appear to all intents and purposes to be AD/HD ***do not meet criteria for diagnosis***. In order for such a diagnosis to be made, and for the disorder therefore to be appropriate for the various treatment regimens, the following additional criteria need to be met:

(a) the symptoms must be present prior to age 7;

(b) the symptoms must be present in more than one major area of the child's life (e.g., both at school and at home);

(c) several other major disorders must be ruled out (e.g., anxiety disorders, mood disorders, pervasive developmental disorders, etc.).

In other words, a child does not "acquire" an attention deficit disorder in Grade 3 or Grade 4, nor show it only in math class. Symptoms that are first noted at older ages or seen only in specific circumstances are more than likely secondary to NLD, LLD or some other causal factors.

Once again, however, many of the treatment approaches suited to AD/HD are also useful when dealing with the attentional aspects of LLD or NLD. Before a medical approach is tried, however, a definitive diagnosis needs to be made, behavioural measures instituted, and extremely close monitoring put in place.

Developmental Coordination Disorder (DCD)

There are some children who are seen, especially by Physiotherapists and Occupational Therapists, as fitting the criteria for Developmental Coordination Disorder, which involves such difficulties as coordination and balance. The symptoms of DCD are described as follows:

Developmental delay in sitting up, crawling and walking
Deficits in handwriting
Problems in gross motor coordination (jumping, hopping, standing on one foot)
Problems in fine motor coordination (tying shoelaces, tapping one finger on another)
Clumsiness.

These gross and associated fine motor difficulties may not interfere directly with more traditional learning *per se*, although they may well affect the development of some fine motor and visual-motor integration skills. For example, a meta-analysis of research findings on children with DCD indicated mild difficulties in almost all areas of information processing, but more significant problems in the area of visual-spatial skills, whether or not the task involved a motor component (Wilson and McKenzie, 1998).

In addition, they may affect many of the athletic and play situations that can affect a child's acceptance by peers, which in turn may contribute significantly to self-image and thus self-esteem problems.

A diagnosis of a learning disability appears to take precedence over a diagnosis of DCD, in that it is accepted practice for other causes or types of LD to be ruled out before a diagnosis of DCD is confirmed (see www.medline.com).

CHAPTER 5

CLINICAL SUBTYPES OF NLD

Over the past several years in our group practice, we have consistently identified four clinical subtypes of NLD, based on presenting problems and subsequently on the profile from a psychoeducational assessment. These subtypes have been termed Perceptual, Social, Written Expressive, and Attentional. While they have some general features in common and some children may show elements of more than one, we believe that these four presentations diverge sufficiently from each other in terms of differing underlying psychological processes to warrant being termed "subtypes," each suggesting separate recommendations for educational, social and behavioural management.

These subtypes may or may not have some neuropsychological, empirical, or research basis – to date, there has been no systematic investigation of this. Suffice it to say that most parents and educators, not to mention many other professionals who are involved with NLD children, are overwhelmed by the whole NLD "syndrome." This leads to many becoming discouraged, and even depressed. We all need to be able to grasp what we are dealing with, and find a place to start. If they serve no other purpose, these subtypes provide a focus.

Our advice to those living and working with NLD is to decide which of the symptoms or set of symptoms is causing the most interference with life – and start there.

Most importantly, even if there is no diagnosis of NLD, or if there is a different diagnosis (e.g., Asperger's Syndrome, LLD, developmental delay, developmental coordination disorder, pragmatic language disorder, etc.), IF THE CAP FITS, WEAR IT. In other words, if specific difficulties exist that are reflected in one of the subtypes, try some of the interventions to see if they work..

Perceptual NLD (P-NLD)

Laura is a 15-year-old girl, brought for therapy by her parents for anger management issues. She is "freaking out" at home, screaming at family members to the point where everyone is walking around her on eggshells, and her younger brother rarely leaves his room When she has a deadline looming – for a project, a test, an exam, a recital – she tends to leave everything until the last minute and then becomes highly agitated and demanding, to the point where she can be virtually hysterical. She is described as highly-strung, anxious about many things, extremely bright, popular, gifted with language, and involved in many extra-curricular activities. Her room is messy and she lives in a whirlwind, and yet, at the same time, she is a perfectionist who becomes very frustrated when her world is not organized the way she wants it to be. Her parents report that she will frequently do her school work over and over until she is satisfied with the product – even if it means staying up late or getting up early, and even when they cannot see any problems with the way it was. She is struggling with her academic level Grade 10 math program and does not have many nice things to say about her teacher who, she complains, is an "idiot" who does not know how to teach. Her parents report, however, that she has had difficulties in math problem-solving as long as they can remember. Laura herself says that she is usually able to learn how to do a particular process (for example, solve quadratic equations), plug numbers into formulae, and remember "rules," but admits that she really does not understand what she is doing. Her teachers see her as a gifted, model student, with all her work completed neatly and handed in on time. She is a straight A student, except in math where she struggles to get B's. She wants to be a doctor in a Third World country.

Matthew is 10 years old and struggling with his Grade 4 French Immersion curriculum. He works on his homework for many hours each night, with on-going support from both parents and a twice-weekly tutor. He had good marks throughout his primary grades, at least until the end of Grade 2. In Grade 3, he began to bring home much of the work he was supposed to complete in school, and his mother soon became aware that he really did not understand what it was he was doing. "Matthew just doesn't get *it," is her frequent comment. He is extremely well-behaved in school, is athletically talented, and is popular with his peers. His handwriting is reasonably neat, although it takes him a lot of effort, but he has great difficulty organizing his work, keeping his binders in order, remembering what he needs to bring with him for his homework, and knowing what he has to learn. He loves to read, especially comic books, and draws intricate pictures of battleships and rockets. While he manages to do reasonably well on class tests, he is having great difficulty with book reports, research projects, and other such assignments, and they are completed only with high levels of adult input, including tearing of hair and gnashing of teeth. His frustration with his school work is beginning to show at home, he is not sleeping well, and his parents are afraid he is becoming depressed. When Matthew's parents approach his teachers to request an assessment because they suspect he has learning problems, they are told that Matthew's oral work is excellent, and that his marks are still well within the average for his class. There are a number of children who are a higher priority for the scarce assessment resources.*

The primary area of difficulty for children with P-NLD is that of ***pattern recognition***. They usually present primarily with difficulties in general organizational skills, including: assignments unfinished and/or not submitted; messy and/or incomplete notebooks; missing notes, handouts, etc.; untidy binders, desks, lockers; poor time and project management skills, etc. They are more likely than their other NLD peers to present with some academic concerns, although these are usually felt by teachers and parents to be the result of their difficulties organizing their work. These academic concerns generally focus on mathematics (especially measurement, shapes, geometry, problem-solving), visual (as opposed to rule-bound and phonetic) spelling, mapping skills, graphing, and task-completion. They frequently have comments on their report cards, or from parents, that reflect well-developed verbal abilities and therefore the expectation that they should be doing better in all academic areas. Some of these children experience problems with reversals and/or sequencing of letters and numbers that continue into Grades 2, 3 and even 4, reflecting their difficulty organizing and remembering visual arrays. Commonly, they show major problems integrating parts and wholes - in other words, understanding that complex tasks can be broken down into small steps, and then that these steps can subsequently be followed in order to recreate the whole. This may relate to such widely diverse situations as coping with letters, words, sentences, and/or stories; keeping track of their daily or weekly schedule; or tidying their bedrooms. They become lost in the forest because of the trees, and do not always see that the trees are, in fact, part of the forest. They have difficulty with spatial and temporal relationships of all kinds, and therefore have trouble with mathematical concepts such as distance, speed, shape, three-dimensional objects, sets, and relationships among numbers (greater than/less than, n-times as many, divided into versus divided by, combinations, permutations, and so on).

P-NLD children show deficits primarily, and often exclusively, on tests measuring various aspects of perceptual organization and part-whole integration. They may show a relatively average ability to discern visual detail, but is usually in the *interpretation* and *application* of this visual detail that they begin to show problems. Most often, although not always, they have great difficulties on puzzle-completion tasks (such as Object Assembly on the WISC-III) which requires the child to make sense of a situation consisting of abstract and initially meaningless parts. Unlike tests requiring the sequencing of pictures to tell a story or follow a theme, in which a child can rely on language skills and social experiences, and on tasks where a model is available for comparison purposes, the child has to "create" the whole from visual images and/or long-term visual memory, while at the same time keeping track of the important details.

Unless there are significant difficulties with the perception and interpretation of socially-relevant cues, perhaps accompanied by other factors such as a high degree of introversion and social difficulties in the family, social deficits are not usually front and centre in P-NLD children. Provided they have been exposed to, and expected to follow, the rules of acceptable behaviour at home and at school, they frequently seem to be able to compensate relatively well by using their linguistic competence and good auditory processing skills, enabling them to internalize and "learn" appropriate social interactions. Mitigating factors appear to be a more extraverted personality, early identification of social deficits with appropriate social skills training or intervention, a highly socially-oriented family environment, and/or a high level of insight into the various requirements of social situations.

A Note About Organizational Skills

It has been postulated that approximately half the world has a sense of order and likes to be organized, and half the world does not. Thus, while order, structure, and routine reduce anxiety in many of us, the rest of us prefer the comfortable familiarity of clutter.

Individuals who are intrinsically organized revel in lists, routines, drills and, most of all, closure. Their brains are an automatic filing cabinet, with a place for everything and everything in its place. Clutter – physical or mental – brings anxiety. Decisions and choices are the bread-and-butter of the organized, and they cannot understand for the life of them why everyone else would not want to be organized. In fact, they believe it is their mission to assist everyone else to become organized. In this manner, their anxieties are minimized, and their world becomes quite predictable and ordered. Children who have this intrinsic need for order and yet who have difficulty learning strategies to organize their information input, are obviously going to suffer great frustration and high anxiety.

The other half of the world – in other words, those people who are more flexible, with no intrinsic need for order – value spontaneity and. would much rather just "go with the flow." They are laid back and unhurried, unfazed by deadlines and relaxed about meeting them. Flexible individuals are not hung up on one way of doing things, and tend to be less judgmental about what is right and what is wrong. Order *increases*, rather than decreases, their anxiety. Why would they make a decision when another piece of information may well come along and change it? Might as well just sit the fence, and wait and see. Lists, schedules, charts and drills fill them with dread. Helping such individuals see that organization is positive can be an uphill task, and can create much conflict and frustration in any relationship – parent-child, teacher-student, husband-wife, and so on. This is the case whether the helper is also a flexible type, in which case both parties are anxious about creating order for the same reasons, or whether the helper is an organized type, in which case both parties are anxious about creating order for *different* reasons.

It is thus quite helpful, and may even be essential, to understand not only the basic personality of the NLD individual, but also our own, before attempting to assist with organizational skills.

Social NLD (S-NLD)

Melanie is referred at the end of Grade 3 because her parents are extremely concerned about some behaviour problems at school, her lack of friends, and her tendency to be a "loner." Their anxiety is increased by recent news reports of school shootings by teenagers who apparently showed similar traits when they were younger. Mel is an only child whose father is a research physicist and a professor at a local university, spending most of his working life and his spare time in front of the computer. Her mother devotes herself to her daughter and is a permanent fixture at the school, volunteering for everything she can, so that she can keep an eye on her. She says that Mel does not seem to be able to handle the school-yard at all, frequently finding herself the victim of teasing or bullying, occasionally to the point where her mother or one of the teachers has had to rescue her. She seems to prefer adult company, or playing with children who are much younger. Her teachers are not worried about her academic progress, although her father feels that she is a very bright child who should be doing better than the bare average she is currently achieving on her report cards. However, the teachers are concerned that she is frequently off in her own world, and that they have difficulty establishing eye contact with her. They report that her behaviour is unpredictable, and that her responses to them and to other children are sometimes quite inappropriate, specifically her tone of voice, or the degree of emotion shown. More often than not, however, she tries to avoid social interactions with the other students altogether. Both parents and teachers agree that she needs assistance. The principal is eager to have her diagnosed with Asperger's Syndrome, so that he will be able to access funding for an educational assistant to help both Mel and some other difficult students in the class.

Alex has been having social difficulties since he first went to play group as a toddler, being the first child ever to be "expelled" for aggressive behaviour. He is now 11 and in a small private school, where the teachers have arranged for a "Circle of Friends" to help him socialize at recess times, since he used to be left out when the other children played. While he is never happier than when he has an adult audience to listen to minute details about the most recent science fiction movie he has seen, he does not seem to want to listen when others try to talk to him. He interrupts constantly, even in class, and does not seem to be able to modulate his voice appropriately, speaking quite loudly, even one-to-one in a quiet environment. His teachers describe him as "in your face," and unaware of personal space. He is quite a clumsy child, who is not particularly interested in athletic pursuits - but his family does not participate in sports, preferring instead to listen to music or engage in other arts-based activities. The family spends hours debating and discussing, listening to CBC Radio 2, and reading. He has a much younger brother and sister with whom he is very close and protective, and he is responsible for the family's pet rabbit. Alex does not have significant academic problems, but his teachers say that he requires a great deal of input on their part to keep him on top of his work, and they have been making a number of allowances for him, since they have found his temper outbursts to be worth avoiding at all costs.

There are many children with NLD who present primarily with social skills problems and difficulties with interpersonal interactions. These may manifest as problems making or keeping friends; inappropriate social behaviours (e.g., "weird" behaviour in the classroom, unsuitable conversation, etc.); lack of understanding of personal space, boundary and privacy issues; difficulty maintaining social conversation (e.g., use of adult jargon with other children, inability to take turns in conversation, etc.); "loner" personality; fixation on certain topics or interests out of the normal range for their age group, and so on. Unless their behaviours are disruptive in the classroom, they are more commonly referred by concerned parents than by their teachers. These children are frequently being diagnosed with Asperger's Syndrome, particularly if they are not showing any obvious history of early language difficulties. It is felt to be very important to examine these children's cognitive profiles very carefully in order to distinguish S-NLD children from those who are more autistic-like, and/or from those whose social problems stem from environmental factors, such as inappropriate or inconsistent parenting, chaotic family background, deprivation, or other related social or behavioural factors.

Beyond the verbal/performance discrepancy, examination of the profile of S-NLD children frequently reveals a low score on some of the perceptual organization tasks, specifically on subtests with more socially-oriented themes (e.g., Picture Arrangement and Object Assembly with the requirement for observation of socially-relevant detail), along with difficulties with tests tapping social problem-solving. Some S-NLD children show a relatively low score on tests of actual social knowledge – i.e., the "rules" and expectations of our social environment. These S-NLD children do not only have difficulty "reading" social cues, or nonverbal communication, from their visual environment, but they also do not have a strong cache of internalized "rules" by which to monitor, plan and execute interpersonal interactions. In other words, they do not appear to have learned how to behave in social situations either by being told what to do, or by observation of others' behaviour.

However, many S-NLD children actually score relatively well on tests of social knowledge, but do not appear to be able to *access* these skills when required in real-life situations. This is typical of NLD individuals who may well be in possession of the specific "tools," but who do not appear to be able to access or utilize these tools in more complex situations.

The inability to process and interpret visual cues from the environment is a significant handicap in social interactions, albeit sometimes quite subtle. S-NLD children may well be able to "talk the talk" but not always "walk the walk" in interpersonal situations. Because of their superb verbal abilities, they may often talk their way into situations that they cannot actually handle. They may therefore have little trouble initially making friends, but sustaining friendships proves to be very difficult for them.

There may be some gender-related issues at work when it comes to mediating factors in the area of social deficits. S-NLD girls, in particular, appear to benefit from the female propensity for verbally-focused interactions as the social focus, since their relative strengths in linguistic competence can sustain girls' social-rules-based play. Boys with S-NLD, however, may well suffer from difficulties in more athletically-oriented social situations, particularly when team play is involved in terms of having to "read" a play in soccer or hockey, for example, or in other situations where gut instincts are important. Extraverted S-NLD children, regardless of gender, can often be successful in the initial stages of making friends, but have considerable difficulty sustaining relationships beyond the introductory level. Introverted children are more content to withdraw from interpersonal situations, independent of the presence of NLD, and it is hard to motivate them to change because of the discomfort precipitated by social interaction. The S-NLD further exacerbates this tendency.

In our clinical experience, one of the major factors that seems to differentiate Asperger's children from S-NLD youngsters is the ability to acquire social knowledge. Children with S-NLD appear to benefit appreciably from social skills remediation, either in a one-on-one, pragmatic-language-based program, or in small group settings with opportunities for role play, and re-testing on measures of social comprehension often indicates significant gains. Asperger's children, on the other hand, do not appear to learn as quickly, if at all, since the motivation to interact is quite often lacking, even in a one-on-one situation, and they tend not to show improvement on psychometric measures from pre- to post-testing. In addition, Asperger's children tend to show many more autistic-like behaviours, including some stereotypic behaviours, perseveration, self-absorption, fixation on certain objects or themes, and so on. Although not empirically tested, our clinical observations suggest that it is worthwhile to remediate the social skills deficits of S-NLD children, specifically by helping them to translate social problems into words, thus enabling them to utilize their stronger, verbally-based problem-solving skills and to learn various rules that govern the more predictable social situations. Care does need to be taken to ensure that the words are not dissociated from the actions. In other words, *in situ* problem-solving is quite critical in order to avoid a situation where the child is quite able to "parrot" what to do, but is still unable to self-trigger from nonverbal cues that enable him to behave appropriately in a real social context.

A Note About Introverted Children

Extraverted S-NLD children, regardless of gender, can often be successful in the initial stages of making friends, but have considerable difficulty sustaining relationships beyond the introductory level. Introverted children are more content to withdraw from interpersonal situations, independent of the presence of NLD, and it is hard to motivate them to change because of the discomfort precipitated by social interaction. The S-NLD further exacerbates this tendency.

It is vitally important to understand the difference between normal introversion, and social deficits. Introversion is not, in and of itself, pathological, any more than extraversion is. Introverted children, quite normally, prefer to recharge their batteries alone, or perhaps with one or two others. They tend to develop deep interests in one or two areas, rather than a superficial knowledge of many. They tend to take a long time to make a real friend, and then may well be quite withdrawn if that friend leaves or lets them down. "Observation before participation" is their rule-of-thumb. Small talk and idle chatter do not come easily, and they frequently do not enjoy or benefit from group activities. Thus, if NLD is suspected, it is important to assess the child's personality, as well as their cognitive and learning profiles, in order to ensure that their social difficulties are not simply part of the (thankfully) very broad range of normal.

If social skills deficits are noted, appropriate social skills remediation for introverted children needs to be geared toward helping them be successful introverts – NOT toward turning them into extraverts.

The following table is taken from the *Student Styles Questionnaire: Star Qualities in Learning, Relating and Working.* Oakland, Thomas, Joseph J. Glutting, and Connie B. Horton, 1996). This manual, which accompanies a self-report questionnaire, is extremely helpful in understanding the differing needs of children with a range of personalities, and in providing a wide range of suggestions for children with different learning styles. It draws attention to some of the similarities between introverted children and children with so-called "social problems."

EXTROVERTS	***INTROVERTS***
Characteristics	
About 65% of students prefer an extroverted style. They are likely to: - display energy and enthusiasm - draw energy from what is happening in their environment - feel more energetic after interacting with people - enjoy talking with and interacting with others - respond quickly – plunging in first and considering or analyzing later – and thus appear impulsive - understand and develop ideas by discussing them with others - express ideas, opinions, and feelings to others readily and often - have a wide variety of interests - have many friends and be easy to get to know - enjoy large and small groups and taking a public role - be interested in activities that produce quick results - like to move from activity to activity and stay busy - enjoy interruptions and distractions - not be silent much and be uncomfortable with silence - need compliments, affirmation, and encouragement from others - prefer talking to writing	***About 35% of students prefer an introverted style. They are likely to:*** -enjoy and need solitude and private time - develop their ideas by thinking about them before discussing them - feel more energetic and focused after spending time alone - respond slowly to environmental stimuli - hesitate, be cautious, and think before acting - have a few close friends with whom they spend time - enjoy working alone - be reserved and somewhat difficult to get to know - be slow to reveal feelings and opinions - be happy to listen without saying much - prefer to think about and understand a concept before doing a hands-on assignment that applies it - pay more attention to their own thoughts than to what is happening around them - prefer individual or small group work to large group work - want a space of their own where others do not intrude or handle their belongings without permission - have a few interests that they pursue in depth

Social Relationships

Students who prefer an extroverted style generally enjoy interacting with their peers, teachers, and families. They like to work with others, who in turn feel comfortable with them. They are stimulated by the people and conditions in their environment. They tend to communicate easily with others and are usually perceived as approachable and friendly. They usually have many friends with whom they talk frequently. They share their ideas and opinions readily and may talk openly about very personal things. They are also very influenced by those around them and respond well to affirmation.	Students who prefer an introverted style tend to have a few close friends with whom they spend time. These students need less social contact than others, and their interactions with others tend to drain their energy. They need time alone and will enjoy being with others more if they have some necessary private time. They may not talk as much as those who prefer an extroverted style. Others may listen and give more weight to their opinions because what they say is often carefully thought out. These students are somewhat retiring and unobtrusive, but they can be quite assertive when one of their deeply held beliefs is violated. This assertiveness may surprise others. Although these students may seem to lag behind socially, they may have good interpersonal skills that are best demonstrated with close friends and in small groups. These students may be pressured by those who prefer an extroverted style to act more like the extroverted students. Unfortunately, introversion is often viewed negatively, and students who prefer an introverted style may be seen as uncooperative, unfriendly, and less intelligent than their extroverted peers. An understanding of different styles can help others see the valuable qualities these students possess.

Classroom Environment

Students who prefer an extroverted style enjoy having a place to do group work. They also like having an area for trial-and-error work and hands-on activities. They tend to enjoy noise, and activity that verges on chaos can be exciting to them. When they must work individually, they concentrate better if their area has few distractions and little noise. They enjoy a visually rich environment that has attractive bulletin boards, wall posters, colourful objects, and books with beautiful illustrations. These students generally prefer performance tests or group presentations. They can handle surprises such as pop quizzes easily. They may do better on written tests if their answers can be relatively short. They need to check their work for careless errors caused by rushing through the test. Although they may prefer to be around others when taking tests and doing homework, and do better when they work in a quiet place.	Students who prefer an introverted style enjoy having a retreat or quiet place in their classroom where they can work undisturbed. They enjoy having a space of their own and prefer that others do not go into their space without permission. They appreciate peace and lack of noise so that they can concentrate. They might even be allowed to bring ear plugs to school so that they can shut out a noisy environment. These students tend to prefer written tests over performance tests. They are able to concentrate on written tasks, including tests. They prefer that tests be announced ahead of time. They may need to manage their time so they can finish, because they prefer to work in depth.

Classroom Applications	
Students who prefer an extraverted style learn best when they: - work in large or small groups and discuss subjects with others, including teachers, who listen and respond to them - are given hands-on assignments and the opportunity to talk as they work - give presentations to the class or perform other tasks in the public eye (e.g., reading aloud) if they have the appropriate skills - switch from one subject to another so they do not get bored - complete a long assignment in stages so they do not get bored - do a hands-on assignment before they are exposed to a concept or theory - are allowed to try out their ideas and then modify them through a trial-and-error process - are allowed to respond to a question with an answer that they develop and elaborate on as they speak - receive frequent attention and commendation from the teacher - are given choices; they want to feel that they have an impact on their environment and that their wishes are being considered These students are *less* likely to respond well to: - lectures, unless they have frequent opportunity to ask questions and talk themselves - work that they must complete alone - complicated projects that take a long time to complete - situations in which they are spectators rather than participants - situations in which they must be silent for long periods of time - situation in which they participate only minimally or in which their contribution is small	Students who prefer an introverted style learn best when they: - work on tasks alone - do reading, writing and research assignments - are allowed privacy and time to think instead of being asked to stay busy - are allowed to work with a *compatible* partner on assignments that are to be done in pairs - can give class presentations after two or three other students have already presented or even several hours later or the next day - are allowed enough uninterrupted time to respond - are allowed to prepare in advance rather than perform extemporaneously - have a schedule or syllabus so they know what is expected - are complimented on their careful work and reflection - are allowed to work in their own way without being pressured to act like extroverted students (e.g., do background research before interviewing) - are allowed to work in a library or other quiet place - are allowed to pursue an interest in depth - are allowed to work in small groups of three or four, rather than six or more, when group work is assigned - are allowed to be spectators rather than participants - learn a concept before doing a hands-on assignment that illustrates the concept - do individual work on computers or with other tools such as scientific instruments - can do pencil-and-paper assignments, such as practising spelling words These students are *less* likely to respond well to: - a constant diet of group work - assignments that only skim the surface of a subject in which they are interested - oral reports and other public displays of their work - chaotic, noisy groups - suggestions that they go out and play with others when they are interested in reading or in some project of their own - constant praise and compliments; can become suspicious of too many

Written Expressive NLD (WE-NLD)

Sean's parents and teachers are all at their wits' end. He is in Grade 6, and has just been suspended from school for the third time for fighting in the yard. He says he punched the other boy because he laughed at Sean's spelling and called him a "retard." He constantly "talks back" to adults and is verbally aggressive with his older sister. His school work is rarely finished in class, and even minor amounts of homework cause World War III between him and his parents. His teachers complain constantly that the small portion of written work that is completed is virtually illegible, and that he spends a great deal of time sharpening pencils, losing notebooks and going to the washroom. He acts out in class, and spends so much time in the principal's office that they are considering putting a plaque on one of the chairs. He is believed by everyone to be a very smart young man, since he has a broad vocabulary and excellent expressive language skills, and won both the public speaking contest and the science fair the previous year. Therefore, his lack of production in class is frequently attributed to "attitude," laziness and/or oppositional behaviour. "Sean needs to put more effort into his work" and "Sean is capable of far better quality work" are common remarks on his report cards. He has been told that, unless he pulls up his socks pretty swiftly, he will find himself repeating Grade 6, while all his friends go on to junior high school. His parents are becoming somewhat alarmed, not only in view of his increasing aggression, but also because he is showing many indications of very poor self-image. He calls himself a "loser," says he hates himself and everybody else, and has started to say that perhaps everyone would be better off if he weren't around. This prompts his parents to ask for help for his aggression, low self-esteem and possible depression.

Jackie, 14, has not been to school in three weeks. Her mom is frantic with worry, and fluctuates between being supportive and incensed. Her step-father says she just needs a firm hand and should be made to go back to school. Many of her problems are attributed by her mother to her missing her dad who has recently moved to a different city, drastically reducing his accessibility to Jackie and her older sister. They have taken her to their family physician who has diagnosed her with anxiety and mild depression, and placed her on medication. Jackie's mom feels very sorry for her, and has reduced expectations at home to virtually nothing so that she does not stress her daughter more than necessary. Exploration of Jackie's school history reveals long-standing problems handing in written assignments, along with poor spelling, messy handwriting, and inadequate note-taking. Her report cards contain many comments to the effect that she could do much better if only she tried harder, and that her written work does not reflect what the teachers suspect she actually knows. Whenever the demand for written work increase, Jackie's marks decrease relative to her classmates. She has frequently been absent on days when she has had tests, and has been complaining of headaches and stomach-aches for many years, particularly on Monday mornings. She has avoided being retained a grade because her mother has pleaded with the school on several occasions, arguing, quite correctly, that Jackie really knows the work, but simply does not produce. At the moment, she is threatening to harm herself if her mom makes her go back to school.

Children with written expressive difficulties form a large, distinct sub-group of NLD. Their problem is primarily with *output*, rather than input, or *production*, rather than learning *per se*. WE-NLD children do not have difficulties in the formulation of what they need to write (this would be a form of language processing and come under the LLD label), but rather have mechanical or technical problems getting information down on paper, despite high levels of linguistic ability. Specifically, when it comes to the Wechsler profile, they show a significantly low score on the Processing Speed index, often with an extremely low outlying score on the Coding subtest. A number of practitioners and diagnosticians choose to pro-rate the Performance scale score by omitting the Coding subtest, to substitute the Mazes subtest, particularly in younger children. It is, however, felt to be important to let the results reflect the V/P split due to the low Coding subtest score, rather than to mask it, since this is frequently a significant indicator of other fine motor and visual-motor difficulties which need to be explored with further testing.

The obvious discrepancy in WE-NLD children between their oral skills and their written output usually becomes quite noticeable in grades where the demands for written work increase. However, parents often confirm a dislike and active avoidance of colouring, copying, tracing, and/or printing readiness activities from an early age. Despite this, some of these children show a remarkable talent for creative drawing, especially when they can choose the subject rather than draw to order, and they often produce incredibly detailed works. This can lead adults to assume that they are just being "lazy" when it comes to written production. The issue appears to be that they have difficulty reproducing accurately from a model, whereas they can generate from within and just go with the flow. After a great deal of lack of success with school-type pencil-and-paper tasks, many children develop what can almost be described as a phobic reaction when pencils, crayons, pens, whatever, are placed in their hands.

On assessment, many WE-NLD children show evidence of a measurable lag in fine motor development, and some of them have already been seen by Occupational Therapists way before they enter the school system. However, the lag may be subtle and may not be developmentally significant, and yet it is often sufficient to interfere with the acquisition of printing or cursive writing skills. It may be especially noticeable in children who are in instructional programs (e.g., some Montessori schools, some French-language schools) that require the use of cursive script from a very young age, since many children of five or six simply are not yet biologically ready to carry out these fine muscle exercises. They have a tendency to be extremely slow copying from the board, or from other visual material, copying letter by letter, rather than "chunking" the material for ease of transfer. This may occur even when they can read the words, because they cannot remember what the letters look like long enough to transfer them to paper. If they are forced to go fast, they make many errors and become frustrated and may often be ashamed of their work.

A number, but by no means the majority, of WE-NLD children are left-handed. Left-handers *consciously* have to overcome the brain's automatic tendency to move the hand from the midline of the body outwards, which for left-handers sends them from right to left. They therefore have to concentrate especially hard when learning to print and write, particularly when being taught by a right-handed teacher and watching right-handed peers. They may still be forming the letters consciously, when most of their classmates are doing so automatically. This detracts from their ability to concentrate on other aspects of the task (e.g.. listening, following directions, understanding what they write, etc.).

For many WE-NLD children, letter and number reversals can be a chronic problem, especially with p/q, b/d, n/u, m/w, t/f, 2, S, z. Reversals are common in the early stages of printing and are not something to panic about, nor a sign that a child is dyslexic. Most children who make these errors are simply following their natural tendency to start writing by making a clockwise motion for right-handers and a counterclockwise motion for left-handers. Thus, right-handed children make errors on, for example, C, S, 5, 6, while left-handed children make errors on Z, 2, 3, 7, and so on. However, for *any* child who confuses the letter formations, or for those who have to check each one out to make sure it is correct, the additional effort required again detracts from what they are supposed to be focusing on and they often get left behind and become discouraged.

Spelling problems tend to be evident, both with sound/symbol correspondence during phonic exercises, and with sight words. It is often reported that these children have auditory problems because they do not seem to be learning by a phonic approach. Rather than being due to problems with phonological awareness, these difficulties are often due to a weak long-term visual memory for letter formations, and to an inability to reproduce them from the mind's eye onto paper. Careful assessment to determine what is visual and what is auditory processing problems is most useful, and can be teased out by the use of tests such as the Slingerland, the Woodcock-Johnson Tests of Cognitive Ability, the Detroit Test of Learning Ability, and so on.

Children with WE-NLD tend to simplify their thoughts when they put them on paper, in terms of both quality and quantity. They may be extremely economical in their use of vocabulary (will substitute the word "nice" for "beautiful", for example), even though you know they have a broad lexicon which they use well orally.

While WE-NLD children show few, if any, difficulties in math in the early grades, problems arise when the math becomes increasingly written, since they often have difficulty lining up the rows and columns, and hence make errors when writing that they do not make when they are manipulating the numbers in their heads. Some children are reported as having problems with reading comprehension. However, careful task analysis of tests purporting to measure reading comprehension frequently reveals that the mode of response is written, rather than oral, which confounds the issue of assessing a child's ability to understand what he reads.

Non-completion of assignments, or failing to hand in assignments that are in fact completed, is one of the most common signs of children who have written expressive difficulties. Feelings of embarrassment or shame result in children hiding assignments in their desk or schoolbag, or at home. The homework book often gets "lost" or forgotten. Parents often report that children worked hard on assignments, and are puzzled why they do not get handed in.

This is only one of a potentially large repertoire of "avoidance" behaviours around written work, which could also include a compelling need to sharpen a pencil endlessly, chatting to other children, acting out behaviours resulting in removal from the classroom, crying, being "helpful" when it is not expected, defiance, trips to the bathroom, tummy-aches, headaches, frequent absences from school. These children are often referred for "behavioural problems" in Grade 3 or 4, or for signs of stress (bedwetting, somatic complaints, sleep disturbances, avoidance of school, etc.). It should be noted that not all avoidance behaviours are negative. Altruistic-type avoidance behaviours are frequently missed, and that many "helpful" and "sociable" children use these behaviours quite successfully for a long time before their difficulties with academics are noticed.

A significant number of WE-NLD children tend to be perceived as "lazy" and end up with comments on reports cards like: ".... does not complete his work in class," ".... is not working up to potential," "....could do better with more effort," and so on. It is probably reasonable to assume that young children are not generally lazy. They do tend to avoid things that are difficult for them, just as we all do. This is not to say that there is no such thing as a lazy child. What is needed is some careful analysis of what the child seems to be avoiding and whether he has the necessary skills to complete that task.

Problems with written expression frequently translate into high levels of stress over homework. This constitutes a whole document of its own, since many children without problems and their parents become stressed over homework. However, parents often become aware of their child's difficulties with written expression when trying to get the work done. On occasion, at least one parent has had similar difficulties and fluctuates between sympathy and frustration. Often it transpires that one or both parents experienced great difficulty in school, and perhaps failed grades and/or dropped out because of non-recognition of this problem. This sometimes results in very high parental anxiety levels, and/or high expectations for the child, especially when they know he is bright.

One of the signs of a true written expressive disorder is that the individual has great difficulty improving his work, either in terms of accuracy or speed, even when offered attractive incentives or threatened with dire consequences. The question: "Under what circumstances *can* he go faster/be more accurate/produce neater work?" can often elicit the fact that he can, or he cannot. The question then becomes: "If he *can*, how do we *get* him to do it?" or "If he *can't*, how can we *help* him to do it?"

Occasionally, a WE-NLD child may become significantly discouraged, and even show a high level of acting-out behaviour, or some serious symptoms of depression. By the time things reach this stage, the child is often quite desperate, and the possibility of a learning disability has frequently not been suspected, let along correctly identified or addressed. When professional input is sought for such behaviours, it is important to explore the possibility of some form of nonverbal learning difficulty, including a written expressive disorder, as one of the contributing factors. Early assessment and identification are critical in order to prevent secondary emotional disturbances.

A Note About "Internalized Messages"

In these days of computer technology, video games, TV, keyboarding, and voice recognition software, there are many children who would simply prefer not to write. It is hard, it is routine, it involves lots of drills and practices – in a word, it's "BORING."

Many children are growing up with the following messages:

> "I should never be bored. I should always be stimulated and challenged."
> "I should always be happy."
> "I should always be comfortable."
> "I should always be given a reason for everything I am asked to do. If I do not agree with the reason, I should not have to do what I am asked to do."
> "When life gets tough, opt out."

Many parents are under the impression that it is somehow mean or even "abusive" to make children do things that they are unwilling to do, especially if parents have bought into the idea that children need to be given reasons for every request. Most of us like to take the easy way if we possibly can, and most of us will do so, given half a chance.

It is very important to distinguish between youngsters who simply would prefer not to write, and those who have genuine visual-motor difficulties. Children who can write reams about things that are of interest to them, or who can complete an assignment neatly and swiftly, given a tempting carrot at the end, clearly do not qualify as WE-NLD. Once again, however, appropriate assessment of visual, fine-motor, and visual-motor skills, is the only way to determine whether there is a genuine underlying problem.

Working with internalized messages is frequently the purview of psychological service providers, and can be a complex process. It is hard to change, even when we want to. Having someone else comment that they think we have done a lousy job as a parent (or at least that is what we perceive them to be saying) does not always accomplish such changes. It is very important to create an atmosphere of cooperation between parents and educators if such issues are to be addressed.

Attentional NLD (A-NLD)

Andy is referred for assessment by his mother during his Grade 6 year at a private school. He has been experiencing some problems with his math, spelling and written work, making numerous errors that he refuses to correct. He rarely finishes any assignment in class and hence has mountains of homework. He is described by his teachers as argumentative at best and obnoxious at worst. He is frequently out of his seat, disrupting others in the class, and uses every excuse he can find to be off task Teacher ratings have him at significant levels on every scale except anxiety, and the teachers feel that his mother is simply in denial with respect to his behaviour. They are completely convinced that he has an attention deficit disorder, and the principal has told his mother that, unless she has him placed on medication, he will have to leave the school. For her part, his mother sees Andy as being totally frustrated because he finds many aspects of his school work very hard. She spends up to three hours per night struggling over homework with him and often finds herself trying to re-teach concepts or processes. Her ratings of his behaviour are well within normal limits, and she claims that she sees none of the problems he apparently presents in the classroom. In addition, he is the star pupil at his karate class, and soccer teams are vying for him because of his excellent leadership and discipline on the field. His mother desperately wants to keep him in a school that has small class sizes, because she realizes that he needs extra monitoring and attention to ensure that his academic skills are kept up to standard. However, she is unwilling to request medication for a problem that she does not agree exists. Instead, she feels that the teachers simply do not understand Andy's learning problem. She is therefore requesting some psychological assessment to assist with a differential diagnosis.

Suzie is in Grade 4 and is described as "cute as a button," and a "social butterfly." While she's not considered a behaviour problem, she tends to prefer to chat to her friends or sharpen her pencils, rather than to complete her work. She loves to bring a favourite toy to school and her teacher frequently has to remove it from her desk or her lap. She does not finish much work in the classroom. In fact, as soon as her teacher leaves her side, she stares out of the window, doodles on her books, turns around to see what her friends are doing, and starts thinking about what she is going to play at recess. When her teacher asks her: "Suzie, what did I just say?" she can usually repeat it exactly, and her oral presentations are usually well-presented, albeit somewhat spontaneous. Her written work is untidy and full of errors, and her teacher often finds unfinished work crumpled up at the very back of Suzie's desk or in the bottom of her backpack. When she does her work, she tends to rush through so that she can be finished first. Although she reads above grade level, she frequently does not read written instructions accurately, and has to start over, because she has answered a different question than the one asked. At home, there are constant battles and tantrums over homework, and her parents are exhausted getting the work finished and corrected before sending it back to school. They report that Suzie is an extremely picky eater, not liking foods that are crisp or crunchy, and that she will only wear certain articles of clothing.

Many, if not most, children with attention deficit disorders (ADD/ADHD) show evidence of poor listening skills, with concomitant problems on tests of short-term auditory memory, and problems with focusing on repetitive vigilance tasks. Hyperkinesis, impulsivity and distractibility usually round out the profile. Increasing numbers of children showing evidence of ADD/ADHD-type symptoms are being referred to clinicians, with the result that medication is being prescribed in an alarmingly high proportion of cases. Our experience has shown that many such children are showing attentional problems that are *secondary* to either LLD or NLD, and that it is important, once again, to examine the cognitive profiles very carefully before formulating a diagnosis.

A-NLD children present primarily with symptoms that appear to be consistent with attention deficit disorders, and yet it is quite common for the symptoms to be present only in school, with parents reliably reporting symptom levels at home that are well within the normal range, and no problems in other settings such as team sports, group activities or extracurricular events. Thus, these children do not qualify for a diagnosis of ADD/ADHD, since the pattern of behaviours is not observed in any major setting other than school, and was frequently not evident prior to age seven. In addition to the dearth of obvious ADD-type behaviours during assessment, cognitive profiles usually indicate strong listening skills, good short- and long-term listening memory, and solid concentration to orally-presented material. However, visual-motor and visual-perceptual tasks are often poorly performed because of very poor attention to visual detail. For example, misaligned puzzle pieces frequently go unnoticed, and minor details are missed when sequencing pictures to tell stories. Thus, A-NLD children have a lower score on the index measuring Perceptual Organization, or even Processing Speed, than they do on the Freedom from Distractibility index that is usually significantly affected in children with attentional disorders.

Minor mistakes in subject areas such as written arithmetic, written French, punctuation and spelling are often misinterpreted as attentional, rather than as problems with the detection of visual detail. Encouraging the A-NLD child to verbalize as he works will often result in these minor details being spotted and corrected, but left to his own devices, errors abound.

Interestingly, the use of stimulant medications, such as Ritalin or Dexedrine, can sometimes produce startling improvements in the quality and quantity of written work, enabling children to complete work within time limits and to produce work of acceptable standard, thus reinforcing the notion that the attentional problems are primary. However, it is important to address the other NLD issues that arise from concomitant, or even primary, difficulties in perceptual organization and/or processing speed that are not resolved by the use of medication, and that still continue to require specific remedial support and assistance.

Some reference material regarding attention deficits is provided at the end of this handbook, and in Chapter 11.

A Note About Active/Passive Learners

There is a need for children to interact *actively* with their learning environments so that they can experience their world by using their whole bodies, their fine motor systems, their visual-motor integration skills, their patterning abilities, and the living concepts of time, space, speed, distance, and varying animate and inanimate objects. Art and craft activities, playing musical instruments, and movement (such as sports, gymnastics, running, dance) are all ways of interacting actively, as are such pursuits as Lego, puzzles, large building blocks, climbing, swinging, and so on. It may not be immediately obvious, but these experiences are very useful foundations for the later understanding of a wide range of mathematical concepts, and for learning general organizational structures.

Many children with NLD are *passive* learners. They sit back and wait to be taught – like empty vessels waiting to be filled. This lack of interactive learning (e.g., asking questions, taking things apart to see how they work, following up on something they don't know by finding out about it, etc.) certainly seems to contribute to their deficits in acquired knowledge, and deprives them of opportunities to learn from experience. Many parents and teachers encourage passive learning by valuing children who are placid, quiet, and still, and who wait for information to be given to them. In many family and classroom situations, this is considered the aspirational goal!

Some parents and teachers encourage active learning by providing discovery situations where children are expected to explore and find out about everything in their environment, learning what they need to learn as they go along. In such environments, children learn about going fast and going slowly; about climbing up and falling down; about different textures of materials; about making things and breaking things; about all kinds of three-dimensional experiences that underlie their understanding of sets, measurements, quantities, speed, time, distance, and so on. It is important to note that, while many children benefit from discovery learning situations, many do not, and it is insufficient, and sometimes even wrong, to assume that a given child will learn simply by being given the opportunity to do so. The learning process still needs to be monitored.

Children who are constantly flitting from one situation to another, however, are variously labeled "distractible" – i.e., attend to everything – or "short attention span" – i.e., attend to nothing. Similarly, children who ask endless questions are often seen as disruptive or annoying, and children who take things apart to see how they work may be called destructive. Adult tolerance levels for these behaviours may be high, in which case the children are seen as "just being kids" – or adult tolerance levels may be low, in which case they may be seen as potentially having AD/HD.

Being aware of the fine line between active learning and hyperactivity is, of course, always necessary. It is worth checking in with a pediatrician or psychologist if there are any concerns about the appropriateness of a child's activity levels, especially if they are interfering with any major aspect of life, such as behaviour management at home or school, learning, social interactions, family harmony, and so on.

CHAPTER 6

GENERAL REMEDIAL APPROACHES TO NLD

As mentioned above, one of the main reasons for describing different subtypes of NLD is with a view to customizing recommendations for educational, behavioural and social management. It is quite noticeable that, in the existing literature, no distinction is made between different subtypes and thus many of the suggestions made for remediation are not particularly relevant to different types of problem areas. There are, however, some rules of thumb that apply to remediating most types of NLD, and these will be addressed briefly, before providing some specific suggestions for the individual subtypes in turn.

It is helpful for teachers to understand that it is not necessary to learn a set of specific teaching strategies in order to meet the needs of children with NLD. Rather, it is important to recognize and identify with the types of problems experienced by these children, and to apply common-sense ways of addressing them that draw from previous classroom practices and knowledge of human nature in our daily interactions.

It is worth repeating that it is not necessary to wait for a definitive diagnosis before initiating relevant interventions.

Translating Nonverbal Into Verbal

The primary key to remediating NLD is to make use of the children's areas of strength - most notably, their verbal abilities. This means essentially translating as much nonverbal input as possible into words. This approach includes the following.

(a) Labeling feelings and emotions, even if they appear obvious to others. For example: "I am starting to get cross with you," "That must be disappointing for you," "I am worried about …," "It looks as if that makes you happy," and so on.

(b) Talking aloud through printing, copying and other similar tasks. "Up, down, up, down" will result in an M, while "down, up, down, up" will result in a W. "The red part goes in the corner" or "I need another blue piece to match the blue piece that's already there." "I'm looking for the one with the circle in the middle and the line along the top." "P - a - r - t - y spells party."

(c) Modeling self-talk while carrying out everyday activities in order to encourage task completion, error detection and memory for routines. This provides an effective means to show children that even adults constantly self-correct and redirect.

Bridging the Verbal and the Nonverbal

In order to prevent a complete dissociation between the NLD child's verbal and nonverbal abilities, it is important to connect the verbal with the nonverbal whenever possible. In other words, adults need to make an effort to catch the child in the act, so to speak. It is far more effective to label a feeling or describe an action when the child is still in the midst of the situation, rather than attempting to recreate it at a later date.

Avoiding Over-Verbalizing

Although tempting because of their overt facility with language, it is very important to avoid over-verbalizing to NLD children. This leads to the false impression that they have "learned" what has been said in such a way that they are able to perform the action. In fact, they frequently "learn" extraordinarily well to parrot, or even to paraphrase, what has been said, with no resulting change in behaviour whatsoever. Over time, this may result in a widening discrepancy between verbal and nonverbal abilities, even further disrupting the balance that is required for competent performance in a variety of learning situations.

Learning in Context

In view of their difficulty associating parts and wholes in integrative tasks or complex problem-solving, it is necessary to provide the overall context in which a particular "bit" of learning is relevant. Unless new knowledge is firmly anchored in familiar waters, it may well drift away. There is thus a danger in NLD children being taught skills out of context, in that they may well get to be very competent in that specific skill (for example, spelling by using word families), but may not use the skill outside the situation in which it was taught.

Sensory Integration/Multisensory Learning

It is vital for NLD youngsters to utilize as many input channels as possible to process incoming information, and to learn how to integrate the information from all of these channels to optimize memory and learning. Occupational therapists are experts in the area of sensory integration, and can provide many suggestions with respect to maximizing multisensory learning. For the rest of us, it is important to utilize the see/say/hear trilogy as much as possible, with the touch/feel/smell modalities also coming into play in some circumstances.

Patterning Activities

The importance of patterning activities for all children, but especially youngsters at risk for NLD, cannot be emphasized enough. Dwindling resources and a vociferous call for a return to "basics" in education have contributed to less and less time being dedicated to such essential activities as music, art and movement. While stringing beads in fixed colour sequences, beating a tambourine to various rhythms, or learning simple dance movements, might appear to be less than relevant to scholastic achievement, these activities are all vital in assisting children to understand and to recognize patterns in the apparent chaos of their nonverbal world.

General Implications for Teachers

Children with NLD learn differently and need to be taught differently. It is important to remember that their language level is not the same as their communication level. They tend to interpret what they hear literally and often misinterpretation information they hear or read. They may become sidetracked by an interesting detail and miss the main point of a lesson or of what they are reading. Their understanding needs to be monitored.

Asking these children to "imagine" or "pretend" may not produce favourable results, as these activities may be foreign to them. They need more realistically-based activities, while, at the same time, being encouraged to develop their imaginations and creativity. Some, whose motor skills are not developed, may have poor muscle tone and may find sitting at desks uncomfortable, especially sitting at desks to write. They may do better when allowed to kneel on the chair or stand, or move to another table when they need to write.

Multi-tasking is difficult for NLD children. They do best with routines and situations that are predictable, even though they themselves may not initially be able to recognize the patterns. Being consistent in our expectations is therefore important so that they can learn to predict.

NLD children do not generalize well and have trouble integrating new information. They therefore tend to fall back on established patterns with which they are familiar, and can thus sometimes appear to be rigid in their thinking and behaviour.

It is never safe to assume anything with NLD children! Just because they seemed to know something yesterday does not mean they will know it today if the situation or setting is different. Just because they are in Grade 7 does not mean they know how to use a planner. Just because "everybody else does it" does not mean they noticed.

CHAPTER 7

STRATEGIES FOR ORGANIZATIONAL SKILLS

It has been discussed in Chapter 5 that approximately half the world likes to be organized, and half the world does not. Thus, while order, structure, and routine reduce anxiety in many of us, the rest of us prefer the comfortable familiarity of clutter. It is thus quite helpful to understand not only the basic personality of the NLD individual, but also our own, before attempting to assist with organizational skills.

The following suggestions are offered, therefore, with the preceding caveats in mind.

Different Learning Preferences

The *Student Styles Questionnaire* (Oakland, Glutting & Horton, 1996) is a valuable instrument based on Jungian theories, and can be used to assess a child's preferences for being organized or flexible. The Manual is also a goldmine of recommendations for children of many different personality types with respect to learning style. In addition, it is helpful for adults working with organizational skills training to consult any of the materials put out by the Consulting Psychologists Press with respect to the *Myers-Briggs Type Indicator* (e.g., Myers & McCaulley, 1985).

Awareness of Our Own Preferences

It is important for those of us who wish to help others with organizational skills to be aware of our *own* preferences, so that we can maximize the chances of our suggestions working and minimize the frustration involved.

(a) Adults who are flexible by personality may have an exceedingly difficult time teaching a child to be organized, unless the adult has successfully learned useful strategies that can be translated into child-manageable terms. Those adults who have been forced to become organized can sometimes be quite rigid about what strategies the child "should" learn. These adults may, however, be far more tolerant of the child's difficulties, and be able to understand how irritating imposed structure can be.

(b) An adult with a need for order, who encounters a child who does not share this goal, may lose patience very readily, and may simply not understand why the child cannot see how helpful organizational strategies can be. Sometimes those who are intrinsically organized do not exactly know how they do it, and may need to analyze quite carefully what their own strategies are before trying to teach them to others.

Fundamentals of Organization

For NLD individuals, organizational difficulties are often much more fundamental than colour-coding or filing efficiently. It is unfortunately usually the case that NLD children actively avoid the very activities that will help them improve their organizational skills. Many nonverbal play activities assist children in understanding the combination of parts and whole that are intrinsic in the early acquisition of academic readiness skills. Many NLD children have great difficulty making sense of their basic, visual world. Thus, they need to learn the very simple essentials of organization that probably come quite easily to most non-NLD individuals, such as: matching colours; sorting objects by colour, size or shape; playing games that require visual matching (Snap, Go Fish, etc.); completing puzzles of any kind; engaging in patterning activities of any kind (stringing beads, building with coloured blocks, etc.). Through such activities, they come to understand the basic principle that the same parts can be used to construct a myriad of different wholes, and that the whole can be broken down and reconstructed similarly or differently.

Encouraging Active Learning

It is important to encourage a certain amount of active and interactive learning, even if a child does not voluntarily choose to engage in such pursuits. The parents of children with NLD often report that their youngsters have always resisted three-dimensional play, art, and athletic endeavours, and that they do not enjoy these activities. It is hard to justify making your unwilling child engage in what is considered to be a "play" or "fun" activity. However, the offer of a preferred activity when the others are completed can often provide extrinsic reinforcement when intrinsic motivation is lacking. Setting aside a little time to do part of a puzzle before the child engages in a preferred activity (such as being read to, using the computer, watching TV) can certainly become part of a daily routine. Keeping the activity time short can ensure that each session does not end in a temper tantrum – the child's or the adult's.

Puzzles to Teach Rules

Jigsaws or other puzzles that are accompanied by a picture model are excellent teaching devices for nonverbal problem solving. It is possible to teach a child "rules" to follow that provide a generic template for multiple situations where a sensible "whole" needs to be made from initially meaningless pieces. Talking aloud is *vital* to assist a child in learning these "rules." "Okay, first I'm going to find all four corner pieces and then see which one goes where. Then we'll find all the pieces with a straight edge so that we can make the frame." "I need a piece with a white corner and a little yellow on it." "Now we've done the outside, we need to find all the red pieces that make up the bus." If possible, it is very helpful to be able to leave the puzzle unfinished, to be continued at another time. This lets the child know that she does not have to start all over again, but can leave the parts that she knows are right.

Prompts, Not Directions

When teaching any kind of organizational strategy, prompts such as "Does that look right?" "Which piece do you need next?" or "What do you need to do next?" can be more helpful in encouraging the child to learn how to process the information, rather than the use of a direct statement such as "You have that upside down," "Put that one over here," or "Now you need a green square." Feeding back a question, rather than telling the child what to do, makes sure that the child is actively engaged in the process, rather than responding passively to direction.

Verbal Explanations of Nonverbal Aids

Flow charts, mind maps, colour coding, tables and other visual mnemonic devices do not make intrinsic sense to those with NLD, and must be explained, **using words *along with* step-by-step demonstration**. Either one of these alone (i.e., verbal explanation or step-by-step demonstration), without simultaneous use of the other, will probably result in the particular strategy being neither retained nor used.

Using a Planner

There are very few LD children, whether LLD or NLD, who can manage without the ubiquitous "planner." It is very important to remember that they are not born knowing how to use it just because one is provided for them every school year. It is therefore critical for teachers, especially, to recognize that children need to be *taught* to use a planner, monitored while they learn, and checked up on, even when they seem to have mastered it. Because of their difficulties making sense of their visual environment, they do not always notice what is written on the board, or posted on the bulletin board. Because of their written expressive difficulties, they sometimes make mistakes when they are copying, or do not get all the information down before it is erased. It is an investment of time to teach children to use planners, lists, schedules, calendars, etc. Teaching them to use different coloured markers for different subjects, or types of assignment, or priorities, can be helpful. It may also be useful to have them pre-list subjects for the week, ahead of time, to reduce the amount they have to write down in class. They can omit subjects that usually do not have homework assignments.

Packing the Backpack

The schoolbag is also something that children need to be taught how to pack and unpack. Making sure they have everything they need is something that they often delegate to parents or teachers. A list printed in large print on the back of the front door can be a reminder in the morning. It can start as a checklist (Lunch, snacks, drinking box, pencil case, planner …) that the child simply has to follow. Once that is mastered, it can change to: "Do you have everything you need for: Snack time, Lunch, Phys.Ed., Brownies …?" Then "Have you checked your schoolbag?" may suffice.

Work Area

At school, having a work area separate from a reading area is ideal. This cues the NLD student as to what is expected when he or she is in this area. Any work area should be clear and uncluttered. Removing all unnecessary items before beginning to work cuts down on distractions.

Setting Up for Work

Before beginning seatwork, it is important to ensure that the child is clear what work is expected, how much time has been allotted to the task, and that the consequences for completing or not completing the task are known.

Homework

An area dedicated for homework is the best approach. This area needs to be properly set up with all the supplies and materials the students will need. Providing boxes and file storage units for organization will help keep things neat. The homework area should be in a quiet part of the house away from activity and noise, and should not be in front of a window or in sight of the TV. It should be easily accessible by adults, but off limits to siblings. While many of us set up a wonderful "office" in a child's room, most children prefer to work where they are not completely isolated. If a child chooses to work away from others, it is important to monitor to ensure that the work is actually being done. If it is not, we need to pull in the reins and have the child work closer to us, until such time he can take the responsibility of truly independent work.

Checking the Agenda

As part of a homework routine, checking the agenda or planner is important. However, it is important for parents and teachers ***not*** to "own" the whole responsibility for this. NLD children are not born knowing how to use planners, so they must be taught, and reinforced for using it themselves. For any of us to use one, a planner must develop some intrinsic reinforcement of its own, and it may take some time before a child actually relies on the planner to be of use. It helps to put some positive, exciting things in the planner, not simply all the things the child would rather avoid.

Teaching Time Management Skills

Helping a child learn how to initiate and complete tasks, and to prioritize activities does not begin or end with homework. It is vitally important for us, as parents, to expect our children to carry responsibilities at home that have the same underlying pattern as homework: knowing what is expected, how much there is to do, when it is expected to be done, how much time needs to be set aside, how quickly to work, how to determine what has to be done first, when it is being done properly, what has not been done properly and therefore needs to be redone, and so on. These issues apply equally to cleaning out the goldfish bowl, tidying a room, doing laundry, making a lunch, preparing for a birthday party, folding laundry, and so on. Children as young as two or three can be expected to *begin* to understand these concepts. By the age of six or seven, the underlying philosophies should be well established. We can teach a child to make lists, use the calendar on the fridge for "deadlines," cross off days on the calendar, and to make use of timers and clocks.

Telling the Time

Many NLD children have great difficulty learning to use a traditional clock, and do not get a sense of the "passing" of time on a digital clock face. Although it is difficult for them, it is worth trying to teach a regular clock face, at first using words ("the big hand is at the top – this means …"), but also making use of coloured quadrants, and teaching one concept at a time in the context of a particular activity. Most children who are desperate to watch a particular TV show will quickly learn the visual pattern of the clock face at that time, especially if the TV does not go on until they do.

Time Versus Speed

Just a reminder that giving someone longer to complete a set amount of work does not result in the individual working faster. Speed of working is an internal feeling – inner "pacing" – that needs to be experienced if we are to understand it. Having children practice "beating the clock" or trying for personal best times to beat their own record are way to encourage such experiences. Giving them all the time they need while nagging them to go faster simply does not work. If, however, it is more important to get a task finished than it is to go fast, giving extra time is certainly worthwhile. Starting a child ahead of time, rather than having them always be last, can help self-esteem.

Encouraging Independence

In general, there are issues around independence for NLD children. Since they frequently have problems getting organized to get somewhere or do something, adults tend to take over for them. When they are little, this is necessary. As they get older, it becomes quite inappropriate. Having your Mom pack your bag for Cub or Brownie camp is quite different than having your Mom pack your bag for your honeymoon. However, the transition from adult ownership to child ownership does not come instantaneously, and it is necessary to develop a way of handing over increasing portions of responsibility in a gradual manner. The analogy of a soccer game can help. As the adult, you may start out actually being on the field with your child, physically helping him or her to kick the ball, telling him where to stand, where to run, to whom to pass, making it easy for him to score a goal by stepping aside as he shoots. As he gets older and more proficient, you find yourself on the sideline shouting directions. Many parents get stuck at this point, wondering why the child does not think of what to do for himself. Low motivation, poor drive, passivity, apathy are common complaints. For the child to take the ball himself down the field, decide where he should run, to whom he should pass, how to do his job, it is essential to let him try. He will not be very good at it at first – certainly nowhere nearly as good as the adult who has been coaching. However, he has to try. He still needs you there for support, but he needs to make his own mistakes, get up, dust off and start again. His way of organizing may not be yours. He may have to learn some lessons the hard way. This is excruciating to watch, and you may still rescue on occasion. However, the old saying holds true. Give him a fish and he'll eat for a day. Teach him to fish and he'll eat for a lifetime.

Maps and Directions

Finding his way around his environment can frequently be a challenge for the NLD student, even somewhere that should be quite familiar. The "*you are here*" type maps do not seem to help, since the child sees his world from quite a different perspective, and cannot translate it to or from the overhead, bird's eye view. It is essential to walk him physically through it, with verbal cues as necessary. "The math class is two doors past the water fountain." Try *not* to introduce any irrelevant information, such as "There's a red door on the left. Don't take that." He may do best with a student buddy or guide to help him, especially in a new environment such as a rotary system, or when he is quite young. Written instructions in the form of a list, like a recipe, can be helpful.

Music

For many NLD individuals, involvement in music holds the key to understanding many nonverbal concepts, such as rhythm, patterns, pacing, harmony, and so on. Sadly, schools have been gradually dropping such activities from the curriculum. NLD children need to be able to do such things as: clap simple rhythms in time to music; anticipate what will come next in a musical series; recognize musical patterns; sing "rounds" or other songs where melody and rhythm need to be maintained despite competing sounds; learn poems, jingles, sayings, etc., off by heart so that they can concentrate on conveying emotion or mood, rather than just the words; act in plays so that they can learn to take turns; learn to perform on a musical instrument (recorder, xylophone, drum, tambourine – not necessarily anything more complicated); learn to play music in a group along with others, so they learn the need for tuning in to what others are doing, and the cooperative spirit in general.

Movement and Fitness

Although all too frequently being dropped from the curriculum, movement, fitness and athletic activities are extremely helpful to NLD individuals. Learning to be aware of timing, balance and speed are all critical to understanding one's nonverbal world. Judging how long something will take to do is a critical organizational skill, and fundamental to time and project management. Determining how far it is from here to there across a room, and maneuvering around objects in the environment to get there, are also critical to managing in a social milieu. Learning to be aware of his body and where it is in space can help a clumsy or awkward child be less so. For those NLD children who do not have problems with fine or gross motor skills, more value placed on kinesthetic intelligence can boost self-esteem and self-confidence.

CHAPTER 8

STRATEGIES FOR COMMUNICATION SKILLS AND SOCIAL LANGUAGE

The following suggestions address the issue of communication skills and may be useful at home and in other socially-based situations outside the home (e.g., school, with peers, in the workplace, etc.). In general, it needs to be borne in mind that children with NLD do not automatically pick up those cues from their environment that guide social or interactive behaviour. They must be taught directly and given opportunities to practise with familiar others, both children and adults. Speech-Language Pathologists can be of tremendous assistance in this domain, both for assessment and remediation of what are called "pragmatic" or social language skills.

Simple, Concrete Explanations/Directions

It will be necessary to explain things very simply and concretely, even when you think that she should know what you mean. This does not mean that you have to talk to her like a younger child, but rather that you use plain vocabulary and short, simple grammatical structures. Since she may have some difficulty with metaphors (e.g., "quick as a flash", "run like the wind" etc.), you may need to explain what you mean or eliminate them where possible if a quick direction is to be given or a clarification is required. We usually tend to add metaphors or analogies to help explain something a little abstract. With NLD children, it is necessary to do the opposite.

Positive Job Description

It will be very important to tell her what you do want, and not what you don't want, since she requires a clear job description. This may extend to such simple directives as "Stay in your seat while you do your work," "Look at me when I am talking to you," "Listen to what I ask you to do, "Talk to yourself in a quiet voice," and so on, that other children have no difficulty understanding, sometimes without being told.

Closed-Ended Questions

Use of closed-ended questions will be helpful when specific information is required. "What …?", "where ...? ", "when ...?" and "who ...?" questions tend to fall into this category. "How …?" and "why ...?" questions are open-ended and can be used when you are encouraging her to tell you more about situations or experiences.

Age-Appropriate Versus Adult Jargon

A fine line needs to be drawn and trodden between exposing her to age-appropriate jargon and adult jargon. Given that she may well pick up and retain some high level information that she appears to use reasonably appropriately, she will continue to benefit from exposure to normal language experiences, which includes adult conversational language. However, she may well be missing the more child-appropriate language required to play with her peers. Children's play has a jargon of its own that adults do not normally teach, but rather that children pick up for themselves. Other children do not always realize that they need to repeat or reword things, and a child who does not have appropriate child-language may be left out or actively rejected. Some sessions with a speech-language pathologist may be beneficial and/or language-oriented social skills group training may well be appropriate at some point, if this is available.

Teaching Simple Games

It will also be helpful if she can learn to play some simple games with which other children are familiar. Simple board games requiring turn taking and following simple instructions would be beneficial. Games of chance (e.g., Snakes and Ladders, Sorry! etc.) are preferable to games of skill if adults and children are to play on a level field. Card games such as Snap, Go Fish, and Crazy 8's can teach simple social interactive language as well as providing skills for interactive play. The book *Deal Me In* by Dr. Margie Golick contains a large number of games for children of all ages, classified by specific skills taught. Letting an NLD child make up her own game with its own rules is an enlightening exercise. This may give you insight into the child's understanding of the concepts of rules, fairness, and sharing.

Gross Motor Activities

Some children with NLD also have difficulty with some gross motor (large muscle) abilities. In this case, we may need to give her some actual direction and lots of practice with such basic skills as swinging on a swing, using a slide or a teeter-totter, throwing and catching beanbags or balls, kicking a ball, even running or hopping – whatever basic skills she seems to be lacking. Again, she may not pick these up simply by observing. It would be beneficial to persevere with such games within the family, even if losing is not handled well. Familiar, comfortable adults need to provide opportunities for children to lose as well as win if they are to manage in the outside world. Siblings may be difficult to handle, but need to learn to be patient, take turns, help each other, and so on. Active parenting is required if siblings are being overly pushy, and certainly if they are becoming even remotely verbally or emotionally abusive. Similarly, active intervention by teachers is required in school circumstances where peers are behaving inappropriately. These children are unlikely to be able to rescue themselves. However, it will usually be more effective to stand behind the child and help her handle the situation herself, than it will be to take over and do it for her. This requires direct instruction as to precisely what to say, accompanied by obvious presence and back-up where necessary.

Reading Activities

When we are reading with a younger child, we need to be prepared to stick with simple books with lots of repetition, and to read the same material many times over. We can teach simple nursery rhymes and jingles, and encourage her to predict what comes next in poems, songs and stories. In order to give her practice with more complex language, we can try using reading materials that provide metaphors. analogies and humour at her level. Curious George, Clifford, and the Berenstain Bears series will all be helpful in that they tend to focus on common situations and problem-solving at the same time as providing the language and humour experiences. Dr. Seuss books captivate children with the bizarre drawings and rhythmic language, and she will learn some of the verses by heart. Books about favourite TV shows will also have some appeal for her, especially an older child. It is important that we read *with* her, rather than *to* her, making sure that she is active in the reading process. We can encourage her to comment on the pictures, using questions to help her to paraphrase what has happened so far and to anticipate what she thinks will happen next, so that she can associate the parts with the whole on a continuing basis. Even reading some comic strips with her will help in this regard - the language tends to be simple and the situations familiar and funny. Older children, in particular, will benefit from practice in paraphrasing the story line of books, TV shows, movies, and so on. Even commercials can be useful here!

Practice with Key Words

In order to help her understand what is going on and to respond appropriately, it is often necessary to have her practice picking out the key word or words that signal what is expected. For example, a "Why…?" question requires a "Because …" answer. This highlighting of key words or concepts will not only be useful in social situations, but also for oral or written questions in workbooks, tests, assignments, etc.

Turn-Taking

It is helpful to give some specific signals when she has given enough information and can stop. Many S-NLD individuals, especially, do not have much of an idea of when enough is enough. This can be done, not only by reflecting this directly, but also by good modeling. The tendency we have to over-verbalize to NLD children does not always provide this! We also need to practise being succinct and taking turns in conversations.

Eye Contact

One behaviour that is of concern is eye contact, and many people get very agitated when a child does not make eye contact, because that is one of the diagnostic criteria for some autistic-like disorders. It needs to be borne in mind that holding someone's gaze too long is not particularly appropriate, and that, in fact, periodic eye contact, or eye contact with some breaks, is usually considered to be the norm. There are definite cultural differences in terms of the appropriateness of eye contact, since it can reflect power differentials, gender role expectations, and so on. Whether we agree with these or not, or whether they match our own cultural expectations or not, it is necessary to recognize, acknowledge, and respect these differences. In our practice, we have dealt with many children who were simply not aware that eye contact is expected under certain circumstances, and we have learned to check this out early in the process of intervention. As parents, we need to be aware of what we are modeling, and what we expect in common social situations at home, such as greeting each other, giving or receiving information, conversing over a meal, saying please or thank you, and so on. "Please look at me" is a phrase universally used at some time or other by the parents of the world, and most of us have taken a child's chin in our hands and turned it towards us. As with other behaviours that we wish to establish, the expectation that the behaviour will occur, and the reinforcement of it when it does, are both necessary, and need to be consistent. Waiting for the child to comply often requires a silent pause – and sometimes we are simply too impatient.

Many shy and/or introverted individuals are uncomfortable with direct eyeball to eyeball contact, at least for extended periods of time. If we can sit side-by-side, for example in a car or on a couch while watching TV, we are provided with a socially "acceptable" way of not making eye contact whilst communicating.

CHAPTER 9

STRATEGIES FOR PROCESSING SOCIAL CUES

In view of difficulties with processing some nonverbal, socially-based information, the following suggestions may help. In general, they all involve translating the nonverbal into the verbal so that the child with NLD can process information in their stronger modality. However, do NOT over verbalize. Be succinct.

Direct Verbal Labeling of Behaviour

Since the NLD child does not necessarily recognize visual, nonverbal cues as to how to behave appropriately, she will benefit from verbal labeling of her behaviour, along with a directive as to what is expected. Examples of labeling behaviour would be: "Jesse, you are out of your seat", "You are sitting there doing nothing while all the others are getting their coats on", "You are talking too loudly", and so on. Unless her behaviour is first *labeled,* she will not necessarily follow a subsequent instruction. Just saying "please go back and sit down" may work, but it will not hook her up with the visual cues and context that let her know she was out of her seat in the first place. This is a necessary insight if she is to police her own behaviour, rather than always waiting to be told what to do. So. while it may seem very obvious, it will help her to say "Jesse, you are out of your seat. Please go back and sit down." Again, it is necessary to emphasize that she must be told what *is* expected, and not what is not.

Paraphrasing and Visualizing

Having her paraphrase what she is to do will provide another means by which she can hook up the verbal with the nonverbal. "Jesse, what did I just ask you to do?" may elicit a straight repetition, in which case, we cannot be sure she has processed the information in direct connection with her behaviour. We may specifically need to encourage her to say it in her own words. We can encourage her to close her eyes and visualize what we are asking her to do, so that she can create a visual image that she may be able to remember and follow along with the words. "Go upstairs and get your red sweater" is an example of an instruction that would be amenable to this approach. For a younger child, the visualization may well be beyond her capabilities, but it can be useful as she gets older, and we are training ourselves in the meantime.

Teaching Basic Manners

Specifically teaching socially-appropriate behaviours and when to use them will continue to be necessary, since children may not always pick them up by exposure. This includes the need to say "please" and "thank you," "I'm fine, thank you," "Excuse me please," and so on. In addition, it is necessary to teach them to hold open doors for others, to eat with their mouth closed, not to speak with a full mouth, and so on – much in the same way as is needed for all children, just a little more consistently and probably more frequently.

Transferring Responsibility

There comes a point when telling the child what to do needs to change to asking the child what needs to be done. "When you are finished your snack, what are you supposed to do with your cup?" will set her in motion to process previously-taught behaviour. If we continue to tell her "Put your cup on the tray," she may specifically wait for this cue before doing what she is supposed to do. This not only increases adult-dependency, it also restricts her ownership of her own behaviours, and we are firmly chained into the loop.

Labeling Feelings

Given that she will probably have some difficulty picking up cues as to how people are feeling, it will be helpful to label feelings so that she can learn to associate words with her own body messages, as well as with the reactions of others. "When you take Jeffrey's toy away like that, he gets very upset. Can you see the expression on his face?" "I know you are angry when you scream like that," "Jesse, I get angry when you .... . Please would you .... instead," "I am disappointed because …." "I'm very happy that …." "My feelings are hurt because …. " "It feels really good when you ..., " and so on.

Modeling Nonverbal Social Behaviours

It is *extremely* important to use good body language ourselves. Sometimes we, as adults, are hard to read. We need to make sure our body language is clear and expressive, and that is matches our feelings and our words.

When we are angry, we need to sound angry and look angry – although, of course, we don't have to go overboard with this. When we are pleased, our body language needs to reflect this. In other words, our children should not have to deal with a double message that comes from apparently contradictory words and pictures.

There are many excellent suggestions with respect to social interactions contained in the books by Tony Attwood and Kathryn Stewart listed in the *Resources* section on page 103.

CHAPTER 10

STRATEGIES FOR WRITTEN EXPRESSION

There are two main purposes in intervening with individuals who have problems with written expression:

to compensate for the difficulties by utilizing alternative means of output
to remediate and find ways to encourage the child to practise and improve skill levels.

As a general rule, it sometimes helps a great deal to think of these youngsters as having a problem with their hands, as if they had broken a wrist and were in a cast. This enables us to conceptualize their difficulties in rather concrete terms and to be creative when it comes to determining compensatory strategies.

Because this is an "invisible" handicap, there is often great resistance to treating these children differently from others in the class if particular consideration is given to these students. Consider whether we would place a cast on everyone if one child's arm were broken. We need to have the courage to take the leadership role by telling the other children that it is basically not their place to be concerned and "life is indeed not fair." It is a valuable lesson for them all to learn.

It is important to distinguish between children who ***cannot*** write and children who choose not to write. These suggestions are for the former.

Many teachers and parents become overwhelmed by a lengthy list of recommendations, and either try to do everything that has been suggested, or become discouraged and give up. This is not meant to be a "to do" list, but rather a range of options that can be browsed in order to find some places to start, or to tackle the child's most debilitating difficulties first.

Assisting a child with a written expressive disorder involves an attitude, rather than the acquisition of new teaching skills or the investment of a great deal of time.

Commenting on Written Work

Children with written expressive difficulties are often extremely sensitive about their difficulties, even if they have been quite obnoxious in their acting-out avoidance behaviours. It is therefore extremely important not to point out their problems to the rest of the class, comment on their work in front of others, or to single them out or put them down *in any way*. If you do need to comment, please try to be constructive and positive, letting them know whenever you notice any small improvement in effort or product.

Evaluating Written Work

It is devastating for these children to have their work marked by other children in the class, especially if they have spelling difficulties, since some other children, and unfortunately also some adults, will often delight in "bringing down" a child who appears to be smart. It may indeed be necessary completely to abandon peer-marking if you have even just one of these children in your class. In fact, there are not too many good psychological arguments to be made in favour of peer-marking or peer-evaluation at all!

Avoidance of Humiliation

NEVER, EVER, under any circumstances, rip up or throw in the garbage any piece of work done by *any* child, in front of the class, in front of the child, or in front of anyone else. The humiliation and damage to self-esteem that can occur are sometimes irreparable. Many parents report incidents like this that occurred to them thirty or more years before, but which still raise the same devastated feelings.

Set up for Success

Please think very carefully before depriving a child of recess, particularly those whose gross motor skills are good and who have good energy levels. The frustration of struggling with printing or writing hour after hour can cause incredible fatigue for children with genuine difficulties, and they need a change of scenery, pace and activity. It is important to set a number of small goals that can be accomplished and to reinforce positively the small steps. Children seldom object to recording their own successes in a small notebook dedicated to this purpose and this type of "success" book rarely gets lost en route to home. However, it is essential to be alert for children who procrastinate with work in the classroom so that they have to take it home to do, especially if this work comes back completed perfectly when you do not see evidence of the same quality in class. If you know they *can* work faster and better, some incentives to do so can be effective.

Reducing Drills

If it is clear that the child understands the general concept being taught, you might consider reducing the quantity of output required on routine drills by having them complete every second question, for example.

Personal Best

Setting individual goals by having the child compete against his or her previous performance is a way to motivate without comparing the child to the extremely competent children in the class; for example, asking for "one more than yesterday" or seeing "if you can beat your best time." Children sometimes prefer to time themselves, if they are able to do so, and often like to keep "records." Be very cautious about public displays of progress.

Reading Comprehension Issues

It is necessary to be alert to the fact that many tests that purport to measure such things as reading comprehension actually measure the child's ability to *write* and not their comprehension at all. It may be necessary to check out their actual understanding orally. It is especially important to ensure that quiet or introverted children are not overlooked, nor singled out to perform in front of the whole group if no one else has to do this.

Flexible Timelines

It is almost always necessary to offer flexible time to children whose writing is slow. However, most children, some bright children in particular, are sensitive to being constantly last to finish. It is therefore useful to start slower children ahead of time, or allow them to start or continue a written assignment at times when they have completed other work quickly and have some down time. Programs such as Precision Writing can help to speed up the slow writer, but require patience. ***Please do not forget that giving a child extra time to finish a set amount of work does NOT help to increase the child's speed.***

Learning Ahead

For children with spelling difficulties, providing a list of "jargon" words in a particular subject area ahead of time can allow them to familiarize themselves prior to the unit being taught. This is a way of preventing the cumulative lag that develops when they get behind in their written work.

Printing Versus Cursive Writing

Waiting for a child to perfect printing skills prior to starting cursive writing instruction is usually a waste of time. They may never print perfectly, and can benefit from learning the cursive formations along with everyone else. Some children however, have never really been *taught* to print. They have been expected to pick it up by osmosis. Thus, in the early grades, it is often worth some re-teaching, which is best done in small group settings. If they have difficulty learning the cursive script, they may constantly switch to printing. If it is not specifically a cursive writing exercise, it really helps if you can be flexible. They often also have difficulty using a pen, so it often helps if you can be flexible in allowing the use of pencils. Left-handed children, in particular, often smudge their work when using a pen or a marker, which adds to their difficulties.

Calligraphy

Surprisingly, children who have difficulty with their handwriting often enjoy calligraphy, especially those who are extremely creatively artistic. This can be incorporated as part of their daily work, or can be given as an "extra" project for spare moments.

Keyboarding

Teaching computer keyboarding skills is usually extremely useful. It should be remembered, however, that fine motor difficulties can make the coordinated movements needed to touch-type quite a problem, so these children need patience and flexibility in learning the keyboard. Allowing them to play games at the computer that require knowledge of where the letters are can often lead to incidental learning and can be fun. However, indiscriminate and unsupervised use of the computer using a joystick or a mouse does not accomplish this learning goal - nor many others, in fact.

Dictating

Teaching a child how to dictate on to a tape recorder can be beneficial. They need to be taught step by step: turning the machine on, inserting the tape correctly, familiarity with all the controls (starting, stopping, rewinding, pausing, etc.), getting used to listening to their own voice. Then it is important to teach them how to listen to what they have dictated and gradually to transcribe using the pause button to give them time to write. It is useful to start with a simple spelling list or a dictée, and gradually progress to phrases, sentences and eventually hopefully paragraphs and/or stories.

Teaching Editing Skills

Teaching all children to edit their own work is useful and eventually time-efficient. Simply having them read aloud what they have written is a good first step and results in the correction of careless errors. (Sometimes you will be surprised that one or two children cannot read back what they have written only seconds or minutes before. This is a whole different ball-game and indicates a different set of difficulties.) Going through the work with them and underlining what needs to be corrected, then helping them to correct it (by re-teaching if necessary) is the next step. Following this, you can underline and encourage them to make the corrections; and finally, the child can be encouraged to find his own errors and correct them independently.

Editorial Assistance

If a child uses a word processor with a spell-check program, or has a parent or "study buddy" to whom he dictates, teachers often feel that this is "cheating," when in fact it can be a useful step in the process of encouraging improvement. If you suspect that the parent or buddy is doing a lot more than simply transcribing what is said, have the child write his rough copy with no regard for editing or spelling, and then hand it in, along with the edited copy. If the child cannot type, he often appreciates a story that he has written being typed up for him. Parent volunteers or co-op students can often undertake this task in collaboration with the teacher.

Spelling

There is little more discouraging and depressing to a child than to get back a piece of work covered in red ink, negative comments and corrections. They often glance at it and become too anxious to be able to learn anything from it. The following may help:

- underlining two or three key words that are misspelled and encouraging the child to self-correct;
- keeping a personal "spelling book" of new words, or words that the child commonly misspells, so that they can look them up themselves, recognizing that people who cannot spell also often have difficulty using dictionaries;
- deducting a maximum number of marks for spelling (say, 5%) on any assignment for which spelling is *not* the main purpose;
- recognizing that spelling CAN be taught and that most poor spellers can improve, although they may never be perfect;
- realizing that it is your responsibility to *teach* spelling, and that most of these children do not learn simply by being exposed, say through a Whole Language approach;
- understanding that they do not make these errors on purpose and that they are usually extremely upset by them; in fact, many are perfectionists and suffer high levels of anxiety over their written work;
- utilizing the resource teacher, if available, to implement a spelling program, recognizing that there are a number of computer programs that can help;
- having the child copy two or three key words two or three times, so that the correct form stands some chance of being recognized and remembered;
- never expecting a child to write out a word more than three times, or the exercise completely loses its purpose; instead, encourage him to write it once correctly, cover it up and see if he can write it without looking, and then once or twice more as an insurance;
- do not to permit any child to exhibit publicly any work that contains uncorrected spelling errors, unless you are *absolutely* sure that you have important reasons for doing so; humiliating or punishing a child, or holding him up as an example of how things should not be done, are *not* good enough reasons.

Speech/Voice Recognition Software

Speech recognition software is another tool of the millennium. There are some relatively cheap programs that can translate the spoken word directly into the written word. However, they require huge amounts of memory and computer capacity that are not available to most families. In addition, competent training is required, along with endless patience, even for most adults with no learning difficulties to master the techniques that will result in efficient use of this tool. Good visual recognition skills are essential, plus adequate or better reasoning abilities, in order to make the corrections necessary to result in a good finished product.

Alternative Means of Evaluation

In order to evaluate what a child has learned, teachers need to consider very carefully whether it is vital for the child to write the information or whether an alternative means of evaluation and assessment could be used. Having the child write what he can, and then going over it with him in a warm and friendly atmosphere, can sometimes provide important insights into what he has actually learned. Allowing point-form answers or (if possible) multiple-choice formats can help, although if the child has a visual-perceptual problem underlying the written expressive difficulty, he often becomes confused with computer-ready answer sheets and strict time limits.

Alternative Means of Expression

In an effort to help children with written expressive difficulties, teachers frequently assign project work that involves building models, creating dioramas, making paper mache representations and so on. Although many of them express themselves well through artistic media, it should be remembered that NLD children also may have difficulties with this type of project because of problems with space, perspective, and so on. Giving them more appropriate jobs to do or roles to play in group work, such as being the "ideas" person, or providing the verbal "script" might be more suited to their talents and strengths, and may be a better way to evaluate what they know.

“Special Twice”

It is especially important for an intellectually superior or gifted youngster to receive special attention in his or her areas of strength that does not involve written work. Allowing oral presentations, construction projects, drama, musical or artistic productions, and other alternative means of expression can often open up a shutdown child and encourage creativity.

Just a reminder that a positive attitude, some common sense, and patience are the three most valuable assets when helping individuals with written expressive difficulties..

CHAPTER 11

STRATEGIES FOR ATTENTIONAL FLUCTUATIONS

In order to address some of the attentional fluctuations that frequently accompany NLD, in addition to many of the suggestions in the previous few sections, the following may be helpful. While they are primarily geared to classroom and other group activities, most of them are also relevant at home, particularly during family times, such as meals, outings, and so on.

Getting a Child's Attention

It helps to use a child's name when addressing her; touching her shoulder if necessary to get her attention.

Ensuring Eye Contact

It is often essential to have her make eye contact ("Jesse, look at me"), turning her chin if necessary (see Chapter 8).

Preferential Seating

In order to eliminate as much unnecessary stimulation as possible, it helps to place a child as close to the teacher as possible during structured group activities and perhaps next to a child who can provide a good model. It is often recommended that a child with attentional difficulties be placed in a highly-structured classroom. This is obviously important for the monitoring and clear guidelines that these children need. It has to be borne in mind, however, that their attentional difficulties will, in fact, be much more obvious in such a setting, rather than in a free-flow, high activity level classroom. This is not the child's fault.

Self-Talk

Encouraging her to use self-talk when she plays or works helps her to slow down and to keep herself on task. This means that the adult needs to model self-talk, and that the child needs to be able to talk aloud without being reprimanded for disturbing others. Teaching a child to whisper, to talk "under her breath", and eventually to talk silently inside her head, will be necessary. This includes reading written instructions and math questions (even simply saying the numbers and the operation required) out loud so that the child's stronger auditory and verbal systems will be engaged.

Lists

Give her a simple list (made up of drawings or pictures for younger children) of small steps when she is expected to follow a routine alone, so that she can refer to it and check off what she has completed. This may be useful for some home routines (bedtime, getting ready to leave in the morning, tidying up, etc.) as well as for daycare or school. The more she is involved in composing the list, the more likely she is to use it. She will need help at first learning how to work through each step, and consistent monitoring until each step becomes automatic. A list that consists of "I" statements in the past tense (e.g., "I wrote out my spelling words three times," or "I put all my books back on the shelf) assists a child to own her own behaviour, to see that it is anticipated that the task will be completed, and encourages independence from adults ("Come back and see me when your list is done.")

Positive Reinforcement

It is very important to ensure that you praise her efforts and her small steps toward success. This does not have to be elaborate or overdone – a simple acknowledgement ("good work," "nice listening," "thanks for doing that," etc.).

Focusing to Learn

The following suggestions are taken from *TRICS for Written Communication* by Susan J. Amundson (1998), which are found on the Internet at: www.ldonline.org/teaching/focusing_to_learn.html. While intended primarily for the classroom, these suggestions are worthwhile for other situations requiring concentration and focus, especially during study times.

Monitor the room temperature. Cool, fresh air helps students attend more than warm, stale air. Adjust the classroom temperature accordingly.

Use predictable, firm touch. When touching or hugging a child who is sensitive to touch, use deep, firm pressure. Light touch may be aversive.

Moderate voice and verbal directions. Simplifying verbal instructions and keeping the volume of voice down oftentimes helps students focus and follow directions.

Place inflatable seat cushion in students' chairs to improve focusing. Squirmy or lethargic students may benefit from an inflatable seat cushion on the chair. Commercially available cushions are of soft plastic, available in wedge or disk shapes and child sizes, and are easily inflated like a balloon. An economical cushion is a partially inflated beach ball. The cushions may help squirmy students by providing more sensorimotor input so it is not sought out of their chairs. For lethargic students, inflatable cushions may arouse their sensorimotor systems and improve engagement in desktop activities. Students react individually to inflatable seat cushions and need to be well monitored.

Use non-skid material in students' chairs. Some students slip out of plastic, molded chairs. Place a piece of non-skid material, such as Dycem™ or boating mesh, in the seat to help the student sit upright.

Allow students to complete written work while lying on the floor. Place the student on the floor with the writing assignment on a clipboard. When students write while lying on their stomachs, it may benefit them physically. If a soft bolster or rolled-up towel or blanket is placed under the child's chest, the pressure on the chest may be calming and organizing for the student. Carefully monitor this position.

Provide firm grounding toys for students who distract easily. Handling firm, spongy toys may be grounding for the student. These grounding toys may help the student focus on the teacher, attend to schoolwork, and sit quietly at the desk. Balloons filled with flour, rice, cornstarch or beans are economical grounding toys. Artists' erasers can be a grounding device. A large, resistive, stretchable eraser moved in the hands during listening times can help students focus and attend. An artist's eraser leaves no erasure markings and takes little effort. Ask an occupational therapy practitioner for other grounding toy suggestions.

Use manipulative grounding toys for students. Small, hand-sized toys with interchangeable, manipulative parts can provide grounding and help certain students attend and focus in the classroom. Gadgets that rotate, twist, coil, and bend may be allowed, but should not distract others in the classroom.

Encourage students to complete worksheets while standing. Tape the student's worksheet at eye level on a vertical surface. When writing in a standing position, some students become more attentive and focused.

Band chair legs with tubing. Students needing sensorimotor input for grounding in order to focus on learning may push their chairs back and rock on the back legs. To help students get this input while sitting, use rubber bands from the inner tubes or car tires or use Theratubing™, and loop them around the front chair legs or the front legs of the desk. Students can push their legs against the band, gaining more sensorimotor input and focus for learning. Attach bands to the side of the chair for stretching the arms.

Introduce simple yoga postures for transitions. For flexibility, strengthening and centering, students enjoy simple yoga poses. They are quiet in the classroom and work well to make students alert and grounded, and to build strength and flexibility. Contact an occupational or physical therapist for age-appropriate suggestions.

Use transitional activities to encourage students to be centered. Activities that provide students "heavy work" (i.e., resistance) may be calming and focusing, just as adults may find pushing a lawnmower or scrubbing a floor centering.

Provide chewy and crunchy snacks. Although food is not widely promoted during class time, certain snacks may help students be calm and focus on their school work. Consider the following chewy treats: fruit roll-ups; dried fruits (craisins, apple slices, banana chips); beef and fish jerky; sugarless gum; sugar-free candies; bagels; cheese chunks. Crunchy snacks are: raw vegetable sticks; apple slices; pretzels; popcorn; bread sticks; rice cakes.

Provide students with appropriate objects to mouth when they are working. Some students will suck on their hair, chew on erasers, place their fingers in their mouths, and/or grind their teeth. Most students do this to help themselves calm and focus. Allow the student to chew on a necklace strung with flexible rubber tubing pieces or a piece of washcloth.

Allow students to drink from water bottles. Sucking through a straw may be calming for some students. Allow the student to have a water bottle with a plastic straw at the desk. By substituting a "crazy" (longer, coiled and looping) straw, the student must suck harder to move the water, which can be more organizing to the sensorimotor system.

A Note About Medication

If a medical approach to the attentional difficulties is to be considered (for example, the use of Ritalin or related substances), it is important to be aware of the fact that the primary problem for these children is the nonverbal learning disability. However, appropriate and well-monitored use of medication can help some NLD children to focus their attention, control hyperkinesis and impulsivity to some degree, increase the chances of them finishing assignments in a shorter time, allow them to produce neater written work, and reduce off-task behaviour. The use of medication will *not* address the underlying perceptual and/or organizational deficits. Learning disabilities are not eliminated by the use of medication, and the associated social/behavioural difficulties, while sometimes managed, are not routinely "cured." It is also critical to remember that there is sometimes a high level of resistance to the use of medication by parents and/or students, frequently for good reason, and that sometimes the use of medication is contraindicated because of body mass index, allergies, coexisting conditions such as Tourette's syndrome, or other important conditions. It is therefore inappropriate for parents to be placed in a position where they feel coerced into agreeing to medicate a child in exchange for the cooperation of the school in programming for that child.

There are numerous excellent sources for assisting with management of attention deficit disorders, and this is not the place to attempt to summarize this huge body of literature. The Learning Disabilities Associations or CHADD (Children and Adults with Attention Deficit Disorders) are helpful resources, and are listed in local telephone directories. Two particularly enjoyable and practical books are: *Driven to Distraction* (Hallowell, 1995), and *The Manipulative Child* (Swihart & Cotter, 1996).

CHAPTER 12

STRATEGIES FOR DEALING WITH BEHAVIOUR MANAGEMENT

In general, there is a need to use the same basic approaches to behaviour management that work for all children: state what you want them to do in positive terms, instead of what you do not want them to do; make sure you are being concrete and clear; use words and concepts they understand; give them a clear set of choices, any of which you can live with; explain what the consequence of each choice is; if there is no choice, do not give one; follow through. Simple, n'est-ce pas? The following suggestions attempt to address some of the additional issues relevant to NLD children in particular.

Encouraging Independence

A child with NLD frequently generates a great deal of support from adults around her, both at home and elsewhere, since the need for adult intervention in a multitude of situations is usually quite obvious. Thus, she may inadvertently but frequently become quite dependent on adults and somewhat passive in owning and/or solving her own problems. There is, therefore, a real need for her to see herself as a competent child - being put in charge of those tasks for which she already has the appropriate developmental skills (such as putting on her jacket to go outside), being coached in skills that are emerging (such as following directions, or interactive play), and being given some small responsibilities in areas in which she is competent but that others do mostly for her (e.g., helping with simple household chores).

Choices and Consequences

It is always important to follow through with the consequences of choices that a child makes; therefore, it is important for adults to give her a limited selection of choices with simple, predictable consequences, from which she can choose (e.g., "Would you like juice or milk?", "Would you like to stay here quietly or go to your room?", "Hurry and get into your pajamas, then there'll be time for your story before you go to sleep"). In this way, she will be able to trust her environment more and reduce her anxiety levels. It is also, therefore, important that the consequences of her choices are in fact available to her, and preferable that the consequence be positive. If you are unwilling or unable to follow through with the consequence, it is usually wiser not to give the choice.

Non-Negotiables

It is always important to remember that, in some situations, the child in fact has no choice. Thus, asking a child: "Would you like to put your toys away now and come for supper?" may be offering a non-existent choice, since the child is free to say "No" to the question, and mean it. Stating what you want, rather than asking, at least keeps everyone honest. "It is supper time. Please put your toys away now." "We are going to Grandma's for the weekend." "It's time to do your homework."

Importance of Not Over-verbalizing

As with most children, it will be helpful to the child with NLD if adults do not *over verbalize* to her, even though her verbal skills may be quite strong. There is a danger of overestimating the child's ability to understand the substance, not just the words, of what is being said. Nonverbal interactions are therefore important to develop: raising an eyebrow, folding arms, making eye-contact, changing tone of voice to be appropriate to the feeling being expressed, taking her hand and removing her from a situation, containing a tantrum by holding her gently but firmly, and so on, are all very important. If you cannot be totally nonverbal, try the one word command: "Bed!", 'Toys!", "Snowsuit!", "Story!", "Cuddle!", "NOW!", or counting to three. Talking to her in a gentle, soothing, warm voice will convey a sense of caring, and will help to calm and relax her when she is upset.

"Chains" of Behaviours

Some situations require children to learn to follow a string of simple behaviours that make up a more complex behaviour. For example, she is required to perform several distinct tasks in order to get herself ready to go outside, or to put away her clothes when she comes inside again. In order to establish new "strings," it will be important to encourage her to practise following the whole string from beginning to end without interruption or intervention. Thus, if she gets distracted in the middle, it will be best to have her go back to the beginning and start the whole sequence over. This is called "positive practice" and helps the child's whole body learn the behaviour.

Advanced Warning

It will be helpful to the child if she can be warned in advance of pending changes in routine. For example: 'We are going to ask you to tidy up in a minute so that we can start Circle Time", or "After I count to three, I'd like you to be sitting on your chair ready for snack." Getting her involved in predicting what will come next in a daily routine will maximize the chances of her compliance. "Jesse, what are we going to do after we have tidied up?"

Positive "Job Descriptions"

All children benefit from having a positive "job description" – in other words, from being told what is expected, rather than what is not. "Jon, please keep your hands to yourself" is preferable to "Jon, please stop bothering people." In this manner, the adults can focus on and look for desired behaviours, and children receive attention for what they are supposed to be doing.

Have To and Want To

For most children, NLD children being no exception, life is divided into "have to" and "want to" activities. The simplest form of behaviour management consists of helping a child distinguish between the two sets, and then ensuring that the "have to" activities are completed before the "want to"s begin. In this way, the child is responsible for his or her own consequences, and there is no need for punishment. "Can I go out now?" "Please may I use the phone?" "How come I can't watch TV?" can all be responded to with a simple "Have you done what you have to do yet? If not, hurry up and get on with it! I know you want to go out/use the phone/watch TV! You can do that as soon as you're done." This approach helps the child "own" his own behaviour, and stop blaming others for getting in the way of what he wants to do.

Further discussion of this approach to behaviour management can be found in *Who's in Charge? A Guide to Family Management* (Mamen, 1997), and *Laughter, Love and Limits: Parenting for Life* (Mamen, 1998).

CHAPTER 13

A FINAL FEW WORDS

Prior to the diagnosis of a learning disability of any kind, language-based or nonverbal, a full developmental or psychological assessment is critical, so that all aspects of the child's development can be explored, and so that the possibility of a specific subtype can be examined. It is also important to have a full medical examination, including vision and hearing checks, and to consider the possibilities of food allergies (e.g., milk, gluten) being related to the erratic and somewhat cyclical nature of any behavioural concerns. It might also be possible to consider the notion that the child may be showing some of the symptoms of Asperger's Syndrome which is characterized by difficulties with interpersonal skills and some aspects of interactive language. As discussed above, the differences between Asperger's Syndrome and NLD are sometimes quite subtle or even quite minimal. However, the more autistic-like nature of Asperger's may require some more intensive interventions, and there are frequently special programs available for children with more pervasive symptoms. Research into the differential cognitive profiles of NLD and Asperger's children would be enlightening and useful.

Working with NLD children can be strenuous and frequently frustrating, since the difficulties are often subtle and pervasive, and the rewards are long in coming. It is very important for parents and teachers of children with NLD to find someone who can support them with many of these issues. Sometimes, one or both parents and/or teachers may *also* have some form of NLD, and therefore require more specific assistance with parenting and teaching, since these are both jobs that utilize a great deal of nonverbal ability. The need for parents, caregivers, extended family members and teachers to work as a team cannot be stressed enough. Family physicians can be very helpful, as can public health nurses, special services personnel with daycare agencies and school boards, psychologists, social workers, family support workers, community resource centre staff and others.

As with any child who is having difficulties, it is extremely important for teachers and parents to liaise with each other to report positive progress, to set reasonable goals, to have an open agenda about what is or is not expected at home, and to confirm that it is the school system that has the responsibility for teaching the curriculum materials. It is not reasonable to *expect* parents to teach academics. Some will, but the vast majority do not. Parents are responsible for valuing education in a general sense, being supportive, providing the opportunity for homework to be done, and reinforcing success. It is vitally important that a child who has difficulty completing seat work *not* be sent home with the entire day's work to do with parents. This causes major problems in the majority of families, however nurturing and positive they are, and incredible stress for the child. It is also vitally important that the parents know that the child is not completing work in the classroom and that something is being done at the school to rectify it.

There are many tutors and tutoring services in the community that parents will often use. It is important to remember that whatever helps the child is the primary focus. Sometimes, it is difficult to be gracious about a subtle or not-so-subtle message that you are not doing your job properly, but parents often recognize (usually quite accurately) that you have neither the time nor the opportunity to teach each child one-to-one, and so they prefer to seek support elsewhere. Try not to take it too personally and try, if at all possible, to communicate with the tutor to ensure common goals. It does not, however, hurt to take inventory and see whether you are missing the chance to help even in a small way. Most tutors are extremely eager and willing to liaise with both parents and teachers.

Learning difficulties have been around for a long time and will continue to be ever present. The thrust in education is to integrate all kinds of children into the regular program, which frequently raises the anxiety levels of the regular classroom teacher. Do not forget to make use of the important network available to you from fellow staff and administrators. You will find many useful suggestions from your colleagues. There is no magic "fix" - just patience, understanding, perseverance, and a flexible approach. A positive and optimistic attitude, along with a willingness to become involved, are the foundation upon which success is built – step by little step.

It is very important for teachers to remember that parents are usually trying to do a good job raising and educating their children. Feedback from teachers to parents of children with learning or behavioural difficulties tends to be overwhelmingly negative, to the point where a call from school can set up an almost phobic reaction in many mothers and fathers. A good rule of thumb is that it takes the same amount of time to make a positive, constructive phone call ("Just calling to tell you that Jason had a wonderful day") as it does to make a negative one ("Jason did not complete his work in class and had to miss recess again"), but the payoff is *considerably* greater. Bad news is received better if it is the filling in a positive sandwich. Parents sometimes need to be reminded of the same rule of thumb!

Finally, it is vital to understand that nonverbal learning disabilities can indeed be understood in terms of basic cognitive functioning and patterns, and that they *can* be remediated. Appropriate programming goals can be set and achieved, along with behavioural management techniques designed to maximize compliance and social learning. This has been found to result in a renewed sense of optimism on the parts of teachers, parents and students alike.

RESOURCES

Amundson, Susan J. TRICS for Written Communication. O.T. Kids, Inc., 1998

Attwood, Tony. *Asperger's Syndrome: A Guide for Parents and Professionals.* London: Jessica Kingsley Publications, 1997.

Golick, Margie. *Deal Me In!* Jeffrey Norton Publishers., 1988

Hallowell, Edward. *Driven to Distraction.* Simon & Shuster, 1995

Learning Disabilities Association of Ontario. *Promoting Early Intervention Project.* 2001. Information available at: www.ldao.on.ca.

Mamen, Maggie. *Laughter, Love and Limits: Parenting for Life.* Creative Bound Inc., 1998

Mamen, Maggie. *Who's In Charge? A Guide to Family Management.* Creative Bound Inc., 1997

Myers, I.B., & McCaulley, M.H. *Manual: A guide to the development and use of the Myers-Briggs Type Indicator.* Palo Alto, CA: Consulting Psychologists Press, 1985

Oakland, Thomas, Glutting, J.J. and Horton, C.B. *Student Styles Questionnaire Manual.* The Psychological Corporation, San Antonio, 1996

Rourke, Byron (Ed.) *Syndrome of Nonverbal Learning Disabilities.* Guilford Publications Inc., 1995

Schnurr, Rosina. *Asperger's, Huh! A Child's Perspective.* Anisor Publishing, 1999

Stewart, Kathryn. *Helping a Child with Nonverbal Learning Disorder or Asperger's Syndrome.* New Harbinger Publications, Oakland, 2002.

Swihert, E.W., & Cotter, P. *The Manipulative Child: How to Regain Control and Raise Resilient, Resourceful, and Independent Kids.* MacMillan, New York, 1996

Thompson, Sue. *The Source for Nonverbal Learning Disabilities.* Linguisystems, 1997

Wilson, P.H., & McKenzie, B.E. Information processing deficits associated with developmental coordination disorder: a meta-analysis of research findings. *Journal of Child Psychology & Psychiatry*, 1998, September, 39(6), 829-40.

Useful Websites:
www.abcteach.com
www.nldline.com
www.nldontheweb.org
www.ldao.on.ca
www.ldonline.org
www.medline.com

ABOUT THE AUTHOR

Dr. Maggie Mamen is a psychologist in a multi-disciplinary private practice in Nepean, Ontario, where she works with other psychological service providers, speech-language pathologists, social workers, a psychiatrist, and an educational consultant. She has been employed in university, hospital and school board settings, and has been interested in learning disabilities, particularly in girls, since graduate school. In addition to her clinical work with children, adolescents and families, she is the author of two books on parenting [*Who's In Charge: A Guide to Family Management* (Creative Bound, 1997) and *Laughter, Love and Limits: Parenting for Life* (Creative Bound, 1998)], and gives many presentations to parents, professionals and community groups. The mother of three now-adult children, she lives with her husband and two dogs on the edge of the countryside outside Ottawa.

NONVERBAL LEARNING DISABILITIES AND THEIR CLINICAL SUBTYPES:

Assessment, Diagnosis and Management

A Handbook for Parents and Professionals
- Fourth Edition -

Maggie Mamen, Ph.D., C.Psych.